NOTES FROM A SEA DIARY:
Hemingway All the Way

NOTES FROM A SEA DIARY:

Hemingway All The Way

NELSON ALGREN

G. P. Putnam's Sons, New York

For Max Geismar

Some of the anecdotes herein related have been told, here and there, before: in CAVALIER, DIAL, DUDE, GENT *and the* NEW YORK HERALD TRIBUNE.

And to Miss Kamala Rao and Mr. S. D. Punekar, for their assistance, the author expresses his thanks.

Prefatory

AN essay on Ernest Hemingway was a labor to which I felt compelled. Everyone else was acting so compulsively I had to do something compulsive too or I wouldn't get invited to any more parties. How is a writer to make The Hot Center unless he mills around where The Center is simmering?

Since Hemingway once announced to me that "it is now 0230 hours," I can make trouble for anyone who asks me to wait in the hall. I don't have to know what hour 0230 is to be on time for dinner.

But after dinner some stiff is certain to ask—in the tone of a bondsman recognizing a bail-jumper—"Well! What are you up to *now*? What's *next*?"

"Nothing, my key-shift is stuck," would serve as an answer but a short chop to the ear would serve better. Yet that would only confirm his suspicion that I must be dealing with half a deck—otherwise I'd be in a respectable field. Such as Criticism.

He assumes that the critic and the novelist are cats of the same litter though of various stripe; actually they are hostile breeds dammed in the same basket.

"We are oppressed at being men," Dostoevsky wrote, "and contrive to be some sort of impossible generalized Man."

The Impossible Generalized Man today is the critic who believes in loving those unworthy of love as well as those worthy—yet believes this only insofar as no personal risk is entailed. Meaning he loves no one, worthy or no. This is what makes him impossible.

He demands that perilous voyages be taken and storms be endured but himself stays on the dock. He reminds us that the proper study of mankind is man yet keeps his own distance from men and women. The goodness of his intention is lent expression, while his conscience is afforded ease, by the practice of Criticism. The risk of becoming identified with the objects of his compassion is obviated by his sagacity.

Yet the greater the creative man's sagacity, the less is his creativity. It is easy to replace art by profundity. Present examples of those whose harsh artistry has flattened into smooth profundity are Arthur Miller, John Hersey, Saul Bellow and Paul Goodman. (Although the latter had no art to start.) Their maps are drawn; their risks have been taken.

This is why nobody raps a critic's door unannounced after midnight: there's a Thinker in there but he's on a tight schedule. He drives a well-lighted route, strapped in by a safety-belt, and stops only at well-behaved motels. And there's nothing to drink in the house anyhow.

But if you're entertaining friends and the aquarium is closed, rap the novelist's disorderly lair—"You in there! What are you up to *now*? What's next?"

You-In-There doesn't know what he's up to at midnight, 0230 hours, nor upon the gong of noon. He drives a collision course, lights out, along an untraveled way. The risks he assumes are the kind for which he is wished failure by most; and particularly by those who never take any. Their most urgent need is to be able to say "We were right after all." Meaning that the man's failure will be all his own doing.

12

Yet the man's risks succeeding, he gains cheers from the same gallery. "We were right after all" now means that they have a claim on his triumph because they've been with him all along.

The practice of fiction involves the writer, personally, directly, and whether he would or no, with multitudes: that's the basket *he's* dammed in. The Practice of Criticisim is a means of remaining personally uninvolved: that's *his* basket.

Benign critics there are. I know of at least one who would prefer to get the best from a living writer than to get the best of him. He makes allowances, in writers of the past, for those flaws which scar all human effort that has nobility.

But we are not concerned here with benignity. Our problem is the middle-aged youth, so convinced the world owes him a refund, he is too timid to damn and too stingy to applaud. Mediocrity is never passive; it avenges itself for its deprivation:

"All these reviewers inhabit much the same intellectual *milieu,* and what they have in common, apart from talent and intelligence, is an attitude toward books and an idea about the proper way to discuss them," one commentator promises proper subscribers to a new review—"a book is assumed to be guilty until it proves itself innocent. Books are too important to permit of charitable indulgence. A book for them [The *Milieu* People] is, quite simply, an occasion to do some writing of their own."

Such injunction against charitable indulgence of creative work, combined with a concession of dependence upon the work of others for something to write about, is not only to demand damages where no injury has been inflicted, but to demand them arrogantly. Talent can spring up anywhere;

13

but it never is dependent. Unsolicited opinions should not be telephoned collect.

The injunction also illustrates the ancestral conflict between the artist's view of the world and that of the Establishment. To the artist, the landscape of commercial enterprise has always been a chamber of mirages by which the true world is perverted; and the *Milieu-Man,* the critic, has, traditionally, been the artist's apologist.

But to Business, Government, Church, Military, TV, Press and Hollywood, the world which feeds, clothes, arms and amuses men is the one real world; the artist is the distorter.

The *Milieu-Man* has now, by and large, become the Establishment's apologist. Whose proof, that the Establishment's reality *is* real, is that the Establishment *works:* that nowhere before has the artist been so widely benefacted. In no other age, no other land nor other season than our own, has the artist been more generously patronized.

Yet he must remain hostile or be untrue. For the Establishment lives in the third-person; the artist in the first. The devastation we have seen, and the dehumanization threatening, prove that the Establishment not only works but that it works too well.

In such a world the writer's single usefulness has come to be the man who lives by no image, let his flaws show naked as they may. For, however disastrous to human values a civilization geared to technology may seem to him, he's in it all the same. And the best he can do, by strength, luck or sheer stubbornness, is to stand in ironic affiliation to it.

The Impossible Generalized Man, The Sagacious Impossibility, either at the levers of a commercial publishing house or a chair of English Literature, cannot risk such irony.

Nor is this to quarrel with the just and necessary function

14

of criticism: how many times Hemingway might have pressed the trigger before releasing it is just what is needed for a fuller understanding of *Farewell to Arms*. Dedicating oneself to a chronological breakdown of the accidents Hemingway sustained, from the time he skinned a knee in 1904 to the time a chandelier fell on him in 1938, shows us that the proper study of mankind *is* man. Anybody who can merge criticism with autopsy is the boy for me. And *Harper's* will pay for it if you type it neatly.

Publish or perish is now the cry of the Ph.D., running head-and-head with another Ph.D. for the widest desk in the Department of Humanities. He'd *better* get attention in print. So, by adapting the attention-getting devices of television to criticism, he can entrench himself in a hard-bought chairmanship.* We understand, when *Time* anoints some persevering wheel as "a dedicated critic," the meaning is that the man has devised a literary image that keeps the paperback stock moving in The Village bookstores as well as hard-cover stock in the suburbs.

So much for Man's inhumanity to Man. Obsequiousness in one critic helps us all; for it puts money in circulation. Theses which establish the respective failures of Mark Twain, Jack London, Scott Fitzgerald, John Steinbeck, Sherwood Anderson, William Faulkner, Thomas Wolfe, Richard Wright and Ernest Hemingway are relieving unemployment of graduate students from coast to coast. For what would any head-on-a-stick marvel do for a livelihood were it not for having inherited a body of flawed art? Back to managing a Nedick's and telling the cook to hold back on the butter, no doubt.

Well, everybody has something he needs to throw up: instant erudition soundly based on servility will turn the trick

---

* See "Come Back to the Raft, Huck Honey," an essay by Professor Leslie Fiedler.

every time. Articles like these restore criticism to its democratic purpose of nauseating everyone who can afford ninety-five cents per copy.*

*

I was encouraged to give a boggling world yet another Hemingway paperback, by the realization that it would be a fresh contribution to write the same old things at sea. I would be the inventor of the very first essay on Hemingway smelling of salt! What the other fellows had been getting into the mixture I couldn't identify; but it certainly was pervasive.

In fact, I'd always had the feeling that, one time or another, they'd planned to write as well as Hemingway but to be better paid. As things worked out, however, they had continued to write badly without growing wealthy; while Hemingway had gone on writing well without going broke. This had embittered everybody.

So I took a book of essays, by one Norman Podhoretz, to sea to remind me, should fire break out above or mutiny flare below, to be steadfastly magnanimous; so long as it didn't cost me anything.

Would my own efforts induce nausea? If retching was what it was going to take to get me to the docks of Singapore, was my thinking, everybody get set for a fast dash to the rail.

The Captain was on my side too.

His crew wanted to go to Japan, but he had a girl friend shelling copra for Proctor & Gamble and they don't grow coconuts in Japan; so they tossed for whether it should be Kyoto or Chittagong Charlie's in Ilo-Ilo. The Captain won the toss. "Make it two out of three, sir," the First Mate spoke up boldly in behalf of his men. The Captain proved himself a sport. "Make it three out of five," he offered—and won the

* See *Man in Modern Fiction*, by Prof. Edmund Fuller, Vintage Press, 95¢.

16

next two tosses. Later I asked him to show me that half dollar and, sure enough, it had heads on both sides. "I didn't want to go out of my way," he apologized.

That's how it is in the Orient, men. That's how it *really* is.

And that's how it was that the *Malaysia Mail* made all of the small-pleasure docks and none of the sporty-O ports. Bound neither for Kyoto nor Saigon, neither would we see Macao nor Luzon. We would tie in only at places where copra bugs live in caves called *Bamboo Alley, Lion of Kowloon* and *472 Cho-Ryang-Dong.*

Happily, my Definitive Essay began with a ring so definitive that, by putting an ear to the page, I distinctly heard something inside *gong!* I'd hit it off! The thing *rang* with profundity! And yet it was so burdened by precepts that its chime rang leadenly and its tolling held no merriment. It was more of an elegy in a deserted delicatessen.

God! Had I but been able to sustain that I-Give-Unto-Thee-the-Keys-of-the-Kingdom-of-Heaven intonation, bookies would have been offering 6–5 and take your pick that it had been written by Podhoretz! Well, we all have our good days.

That one bad night can ruin. Such as one when, through an ominous tenement on the quais of Calcutta, a schizoid seaman pursued me under the delusion that I was a salami requiring slicing and he had the knife. Though I remained unsliced, my grasp of the concept that the proper study of mankind is man was shaken.

Later, while trying to dispose of a watch engraved *77 Jewelries* (purchased in a free-trade port), my bowlines were severed and the Definitive Essay began drifting to sea. I bartered my Podhoretz essays for a pair of sandals to a boatman afflicted by elephantiasis—where else could I have picked up a pair so cheap?

Any reader assuming that memoirs of some moveable feast

17

are offered here, should be advised that, by the time I got to Paris, nothing remained but empty napkin-rings on the grass.

I met Hemingway only once, and briefly. My only claim to his friendship is that nocturnal message: "it is now 0230 hours."

Yet, as he had once observed that all his life he had been peddling vitality, he surely would have understood my defection from critics peddling sterility.

NELSON ALGREN

June 21, 1962: Two Hours Out of the Port of Seattle

Sooner or later, on her first trip out or her hundredth, every ship carries a doomed man.

For the *Malaysia Mail* this was the sixty-first time out of the barn and she labored like a mare too tightly reined; too old to whip, too mean to whinny. I watched her harbor-home going blind in a mist behind her.

There blue fogs kept bending red roses to rest; and girls, coming home from school, kept tossing their ponytails. No wonder the old scow kept grieving.

For doomful seas from the black edge of the world would come rolling through nights without a moon: no ocean had ever darkened so lonesomely.

"Don't take things so hard, Pacific," I consoled the poor brute—"girls come home from school in Malaysia too." It wasn't my first time out of the barn either.

Lights of the rigging came on high and flickering. Then the big low lamps of the staterooms began burning too steadily. Was there somebody else aboard?

I took a turn around the deck to a door marked PURSER, knocked, and got a direct command from the other side:

"Turn the handle!"

So *that* was how these things worked.

He was all officer. Under a cap so bound with braid I saw *it* had made the decision to go to sea and was only accompanied by the man below for his use as an interpreter. Why would a man be wearing such a self-important hat alone in his cabin unless he'd been practicing the hand salute in preparation for World War III?

There won't be time for that this time, sir, I wanted to assure him, as he introduced himself.

"*Mister* Manning," he let me know—and just by the way he told it I knew I need not fear mutiny on this trip.

"Algren," I identified myself, for he needed cheering up. The paperback he'd put down was *Japanese Simplified*.

Two Japanese lovelies stood framed on his desk. Neither looked simplified.

"How much time ashore will we have in Kyoto?" I inquired casually.

"We aren't going to Kyoto," he let me know, "but you'll get a good view of the coastline at Hokkadate."

The coastline at Hokkadate wasn't what I had in mind.

"Will I be able to go ashore there?"

"We only stop at Hokkadate to refuel," *Mister* Manning told me, "but believe me when I tell you—you're better off staying aboard. The less you see of Asia the better off you'll be."

"Did you take these from the upper deck?" I inquired about the lovelies—one signed *With All My Love—Noriko* and the other *To Bill With All My Heart—Suzi*.

"They run a hotel for me in Kyoto," he assured me stiffly.

And throw the profits to you from the dock tied in a silk kimono, I assumed—but which one did the throwing? I concluded it must be Noriko because she had a chin like Whitey Ford's.

20

"These people aren't like us," Manning informed me, "they steal everything they can get their hands on."

I was pleased to learn Americans had given up stealing manually.

"All I had in mind was to take a few shots to prove to friends I've been out of town," I explained, "if the Captain is afraid I'll delay the ship I'll use a Polaroid."

He picked up the paperback that simplified Japanese lovelies.

"I hope you won't be disappointed in not getting ashore in Japan," Manning hoped; looking tickled pink.

If you went ashore you'd be trapped by enemies, seemed to be Manning's thinking; and if you stayed aboard friends might trap you. He hadn't gotten far enough in his plans to arrange entrapment by himself, yet seemed to be working toward some such arrangement.

"It's alright," I assured him. "Don't let me interfere with the ship's schedule. Just go ahead and refuel at any port you feel like."

Manning bestowed his Be-Kind-To-Our-Only-Passenger-He-May-Be-Related-To-The-Front-Office smile upon me. He had a mug as round as a rhubarb pie and the smile seemed to *drip* through the juice.

I had no way of knowing that anyone with a face so self-satisfied could be doomed.

June 22nd

This is one hell of a big ship. Wandering among freight cars in the fantail, I figured out that the reason they weren't rolling around the deck must be because somebody had had the foresight to button down their wheels. This would require very strong buttons in a monsoon, I realized, and went up to the point of the ship to see what other cargo I was being held responsible for.

The *point* of a ship is its front part. The reason for making a ship pointed is twofold: it makes the distance between ports shorter and prevents bumping when you run over a whale. Whales often sleep on top of the water because everybody goes to bed earlier in the Pacific than in the Atlantic. Unfortunately it wasn't yet my bedtime. I went to find the Captain to see where he needed me most.

I saw a fellow standing at a steering wheel and went into the cabin to see why he didn't sit down. The reason he wasn't sitting down was because he had to stand up to see over the wheel. He said he was a second mate and I told him I'd been married once myself. He asked me whether I'd like to try steering the ship but he didn't mention pay. Nevertheless I took over as he looked like he needed some rest.

I realized my responsibility: forty seamen and twelve officers, most of them with sweethearts or wives, were now depending on me not to hit anything. There was a clock that had lost one hand above the wheel and, whenever the wheel swung a bit, the clock's hand swung a little too. I put all my strength into holding our course steady as she goes.

"You don't have to bear down," the Second Mate let me know, "it's automatic"—and a fearsome blast just overhead nearly took off my ears, the wheel swung, the clock's hand boggled, the deck tilted.

"We're sinking, sir," I reported calmly.

"That was just the foghorn," the Second Mate informed me with the wannest of wan smiles, "it's automatic too."

I let him take the wheel back. I didn't yet know that Danielsen's smile, so thin so faint, happened only in moments of his highest exuberance. The rest of the time he lived in some sunless world bereft of everything but memories out of years long gone. Though not yet forty, loneliness had aged him by twenty years more.

"How long have you been at sea?" I asked him.

"Since I've been born," he told me—and again that smile, so wan and wandering. If Danielsen wasn't the loneliest Second Mate on the Pacific they must be flying them in from Antarctica.

"Is there anything to drink aboard?" I asked him.

He whispered something (as he whispered almost everything) that sounded like "Communications Officer."

Communications Officer Concannon sat, earphones clamped to the perpetual *beep-bop-jot-jot*—then rose to six-foot-three to give me a big hand and grin, toss off the phones and begin pouring gin.

"I saw you come aboard," he told me. " 'There's one in every crowd,' I thought, 'and two on every ship.' "

"One of *what?*"

"Why, one mark of course," he smiled, picked up a stained deck, shuffled and gave them to me to cut; then dealt seven hands of draw poker.

"Tell me what you need and I'll match it," he promised.

"Match my Jack."

He dealt around the board and a Jack fell on my hand. Not bad.

He placed my forefinger across the top of my cards—"You're signaling me for an Ace," and moved the finger down, between the top and the middle of the face-down card—"King." The finger dead-center was for a Queen. Beneath that indicated a Jack, and the finger at the card's bottom asked for a Ten. Moving back up, but using two fingers, defined every card down to a Deuce: for which the signal was a small sweeping motion of the card.

When I'd mastered the signals, Sparks gave me one admonishing word: "It all depends on the crimp I put in the deck. If the man beside me don't cut them at the crimp, it don't work. You sit opposite me so it don't look like cahoots. Now how about a couple hands of blackjack?"

I must have looked apprehensive because he grinned like a wolf.

"Don't you trust me, old buddy?"

"I trust everybody," I assured Concannon, "but I'll cut them twice just for luck."

*

"I've sailed with Manning before," Concannon filled me in, "I'm ready to drop the subject when you are."

The subject dropped of its own dead weight.

Both Manning and Concannon are heavy boys, and each has naval service in World War II. There the resemblance ceases. No two men could be more American and no two men could be more different.

Concannon is "Sparks" or "Sparky" to the crew. Manning is "Acting Corporal." Manning conducts himself toward the men confident that he is both loved and feared by them. Yet their respect for him is perfunctory: as ship's storekeeper he can inconvenience them.

24

"You can run your poker game," Manning has told Able Seaman Gary ("Crooked-Neck") Smith, "so long as you run it just for the crew."

Smith had played it safe. "Yes, sir," he'd assured Manning. Then he'd gone to Sparks.

"You and Danielsen can't play any more," he'd reported to Concannon.

Concannon had gone directly to Manning.

"Let's go see the old man about this," he'd offered.

Manning, of course, had had to decline. The purser has neither responsibility for the crew nor authority over them; and that had put an end to the matter.

Sparks, on the other hand, with the most responsible job aboard, appears to have no concern other than, "Where's the deck? Who's got the gin?" He conceals a high competence by flaunting his flaws. While Manning pretends he's a seaborne executive, Concannon makes himself out as the ship's outstanding sadsack. Neither man, when they pass each other on deck, raps to the other.

"I tried to touch Manning for ten bucks," Muncie, a crew pantryman, complains with a speech impediment, " 'n he asks me. Why don't I take advance. On my next draw. 'Had I a draw comin' I wouldn't. Be trying to borrow off you. Personally. Would I?' I asked him. 'N walk away."

"You should have gone to Sparky," Chief Crew-Pantryman Bridelove advises Muncie, "has Sparky got it, you can have it."

"Manning made forty thousand dollars one year," I filled both men in.

"How do *you* know?" Bridelove asked.

"He told me so."

"And he didn't spend. A dime of it. On me," Muncie mourned.

Concannon was brought up, after a manner of speaking, by

relatives more or less distant, around Kingfisher, Oklahoma, in the dust-storm years; never had a home until somebody slipped a pair of headphones over his ears in 1941. Since then, while the hair has thinned, his home has been a radio shack.

And all the brothels, small and great, of the great East China Sea.

From Bugis Street in Singapore to Cebu of the blue-mist Philippines, Sparks has left enough empty gin-fifths behind him to capsize the *Malaysia Mail*.

Forever friendly, cheerful by the hour, dry, jocular, ready for anything, Concannon yet disclaims friendship. "The word 'friend' isn't in my book," he assured me, "the only things a seaman can depend upon are money and whiskey, because money and whiskey gets you the women—and what else is there besides women?"

"You don't want women because you're a seaman," I suggested, "you're a seaman because you want women."

"All I want," he skipped the suggestion, "is all the fun I can handle, and then go out at sea. I don't want to be buried on land. The last stitch through the nose and over the rail, *that's* the burial for me."

"You're putting me on," I told Concannon.

"Why? What have I got to lose? Pussy brought me here and pussy's going to take me away."

"I don't know what brought you here and I'm sure you're right about what will take you away. Only that wasn't what I meant. I meant the last stitch being through the nose."

Concannon gave me a look so cold I was startled. I'd never seen a man turn unfriendly so fast.

"Ask someone else," he instructed me, and clamped on his headphones.

I was dismissed.

26

June 27th: Lions, Lionesses, Deadbone Crunchers

In December of 1955, I bought a bag of un-shelled peanuts in Miami and went into a strip-tease house, but I never saw the strip-tease. It was one of those places that show a film between stage shows, and the picture had just started when I came in. It was *The African Lion,* a Disney production.

It was the kind of house that always needs airing because it never closes long enough to open the doors. So many home-less men had slept here all night, to wake when the girls danced on, then had returned to sleep: to wake, to sleep, till sleep and waking were one. Now the stale death of their min-gled breath hung waiting forever for girls to come dancing.

A bear-sized creature was hibernating in the seat in front of mine, with some kind of sun-helmet dangling off the back of his head. When his head lolled, the helmet rolled around the seat's curving back. It must be strapped to The Bear's neck, I decided, and dropped a handful of peanut shells into it.

On the screen, two lionesses were stalking some horned grass-chompers.

"What's *them,* honey?" a girl behind me asked her escort.

"Them is elks, Baby," I heard him tell her, in a voice so authoritative there was no use contradicting it.

One lioness cut off the escape-route: now the girls had the herd entrapped. As the other charged, The Bear sat up and hollered "Look out!"—but too late. Just as in Miami, the prey never escapes. The Bear jammed his helmet down over his ears and began to eat a banana. What country did he think he was in? I wondered. I tapped him on the shoulder. He swiveled about.

"What country you think you're in?" I asked.

"What country *you* think *you're* in?" he challenged me brilliantly.

"Take off the lid, Dummy," the Elk Authority came to my support.

The Bear took the lid off and went back to sleep without finishing the banana. Some Bear.

Now on the screen a new prey appeared: a rhinoceros. Yet it wasn't a lioness that had gotten *him.* It was quicksand.

How Disney had induced that brute to lie down just there, when it had all the rest of Africa to rub its back in, is a trade secret I'm not free to disclose. In no time at all every hyena in Tanganyika was milling around, pleased as possible to be working as an extra again.

The hyena has two distinctions: he doesn't want to be first to try anything and he smells worse than everything. "You can't be *too* careful" is the essence of Hyena-Think. He feels his smell is a fringe benefit.

A buzzard is better. Every buzzard projects an image of himself as Top-Buzzard. He doesn't wait for the next buzzard to make the action. Where the hyena will settle for standing room only, the buzzard entitles himself to front-row center. When *they* came down, the hyenas didn't stop to ask to see their stubs. They hightailed for the back rows and began milling around.

28

"How come you birds always get seats front-row center?" they wanted to know from a safe distance, "when we're better-looking?"

"We smell so nice we *deserve* front-row seats," the buzzards explained.

Which goes to show you that no matter how bad you may smell, someone always smells worse.

All of a sudden the rhino went all out to raise himself out of that bog. It looked, for a moment, as though he might make it; until his very power worked against him and he began sinking slowly onto his side. The Bear came to and saw what was happening. "Dig a hole!" he hollered—whether to the rhino, the buzzards or the hyenas I still don't know.

The-Biggest-Buzzard-Of-All hung one moment on the wing-spreading air, watching his shadow enshroud the rhino—then plummeted with talons outspread and somebody popped me in the left ear with a piece of popcorn.

It didn't hurt.

The Bear jammed his helmet down over his ears.

"Take off the lid, Dummy."

I didn't want to go through all that again. I got up and walked out.

The first thing I noticed, back on the street, was that the lionesses had begun wearing the manes. I had a chocolate phosphate under a ryebread tree and took the next ship to Havana.

Cuba was the first single-crop country I'd seen. I walked around Havana two days eating bananas before I realized bananas weren't the country's single crop.

Girls! *That* was Cuba's single crop. Girls waiting in taxis, girls waiting on corners, girls waiting in hotel lobbies; girls waiting in doorways, strolling the tables of the Tropicana or waiting in front of funeral parlors; girls in the shadows of the skyscrapers of Vedado; girls waiting in drugstores and meat markets; girls waiting in bars and girls with no places to wait: these were just walking around. Girls waiting for seamen and soldiers.

Girls to whom the sweet cane had brought only bitterness. In stores that sold nothing they waited for anything.

One whose hair was platinum blond yet black as the devil at the roots, invited me to step into her Nothing-Anything door. An American was studying the jukebox, preparing to invest; but he wanted an American song for *his* investment. When he finished reading the Spanish numbers he finally found one on the American side. It was the very one *I* would have picked had it been *my* quarter:

> *I wouldn't trade the silver*
> *In my mother's hair*
> *For all the gold in the world—*

I've felt sentimental about that song ever since a so-long-ago rainy afternoon when I skipped an algebra class to hear a baritone sing it at the Haymarket Burlesk and Miss June St. Clair came down the runway immediately after and shook all the Algebra out of my head for keeps:

> *God gave us mothers and tried to be fair*
> *When he gave me mine I got more than my share.*

I asked the young lady if she would care to go steady with me, but she nodded toward the investor: she was promised to another. Any man who could spend a quarter in a jukebox would make her a better provider than I would, I realized, and I left. I hope they found happiness.

I recalled then that I was supposed to visit the Hemingways. Not that anyone had sent for me. But every American visitor to Havana who'd read a book was supposed to storm the Hemingways with the news. If you hadn't read one you were interviewing for the *Chicago Tribune*.

I phoned and told Mary Hemingway I'd seen a good movie in Havana, so she said come out right away—if I weren't interviewing for the *Chicago Tribune*.

Hemingway was sitting up in bed looking like John McGraw atoning from something; he wasn't atoning but he was abstaining, and invited me to help myself to the Scotch.

"How's the work going?" I asked him.

"I never turned the horse loose and let her run until this book," he told me—"but we are so far ahead now that it is pitiful. The next time they're going to give the money back in the mutuels."

He nodded toward the bottle beside his bed. Its label read: *Best Scotch Procurable*. "I can only have one an hour," he explained, "doctor's orders. You go ahead."

I went ahead.

A lion commanded one wall. Some sort of moose held an entire shelf of leatherbound Dickens at bay. On a wall all its own, like a sea all its own, a swordfish had room to zoom: or, if it would rather, just to sail around. A buffalo looked as if it had just thrust its head through the wall. Perhaps the rest of him was standing outside.

Every brute in the room seemed to proclaim its right to command, zoom, hold at bay or just sail around.

"You've got everything around here but a werewolf," I observed, trying to sound disappointed.

"Why go after small game?" Hemingway asked.

"I don't even run rabbits myself," I explained, "I go to movies instead. I just saw one where a rhinoceros got trapped in quicksand. Hyenas came around. You know what the worst thing about the hyena is?"

31

NOTES FROM A SEA DIARY

"I don't go to movies any more," he told me, "but I still go to fights."

"I'll tell you—it's the smell. Actually, of course, I couldn't smell a hyena in the movie, but you could tell, just by *looking* at him, how bad he smelled."

"The smartest fighter I ever saw was Leonard," Hemingway decided. "I never wrote a story about him."

Hemingway didn't want to talk about hyenas. He wanted to talk about fighters. I didn't want to talk about fighters. I wanted to talk about hyenas. It was *his* Scotch.

"A fellow named Nate Bolden whipped Zale twice one winter in the White City ring," I went along, "that was before the war. One night after the war, I caught a cab on the Southside and noticed that the driver was the same Bolden. 'I saw you beat Zale,' I told him.

" 'Which one was he?' Bolden asked me. He wasn't punchy. He'd just never bothered learning the names of the men he'd fought. Some had been white; some black. At 160 pounds he'd whipped top-ranking light-heavies. Now he was driving a cab."

I'd thought that was a good story but it hadn't come off.

Hemingway regarded me thoughtfully. Hemingway was a thoughtful-looking fellow.

"Go ahead," he said, "help yourself."

It was pretty good Scotch. In fact, it *was* the Best Procurable.

"Everybody thought Leonard would whip Britton," Hemingway recalled, "because Leonard was smarter than everybody and Britton wasn't smarter than anybody. But after Britton had whipped him, I asked him what he thought of Leonard. Britton said Leonard was the smartest fighter he'd ever been up against—'He was thinking all the time in there,'

32

Britton told me, 'and all the time he was thinking, I was busting hell out of him.' I put *that* in a story," Hemingway added.

"A Lithuanian named Radek had Cerdan out on the ropes in Chicago, but the bell saved Cerdan," I remembered, "and Cerdan got the decision even though he didn't know who was holding up his hand. Later he said it was an improper way to win. That's the very word he used—'improper.' "

"Carpentier liked to use words, too," Hemingway told me. "When he whipped Bombardier Billy Wells he said, 'Vice, as vice, is bad. But viciousness in the ring is essential.' What he meant was that Wells had had him the first round and let him go. So Carpentier knocked him out in the second."

The lion looked at the bison. The bison looked at the elk. All three were agreeing on something.

"Battling Siki was paid off to lose to Carpentier," Hemingway wanted me to know, "and the nigger knocked him cold."

I didn't know how to get back to my rhinoceros.

"Jack Delaney's real name was Ovila Chapdelaine," Hemingway went on, "he gave Oom-Paul Berlenbach the business. Do you know what the business is?"

I didn't know what the business was. I hadn't even known Oom-Paul was sick.

"Delaney was holding a druggist's pestle in the thumb of his glove," Hemingway explained. "He stood with his back to the ropes, waiting for the judge's decision and a second took the piece out of his glove, and he got the decision. That was 'the business.' "

"Well, it wouldn't have looked very good, when the ref was holding up Delaney's hand, for a hunk of iron to drop out of it, would it?" I inquired. I had to get off this boxing thing before the man confused me with George Plimpton.

33

But Hemingway only looked at me as though trying to decide something.

It was the Best Procurable alright. If it had been any better it wouldn't have been procurable at all. The distiller would have kept it all for himself.

Somebody behind me was eyeing me. I turned fast. That damned swordfish.

"You were saying something about somebody getting caught in quicksand," Hemingway reminded me. "How'd he get out?"

"It was a rhinoceros," I remembered. "Darryl Zanuck had dug this pit in Africa and pushed the brute into it. He must have had help. The hyenas came around. You know what the worst thing about a hyena is?"

"You told me. Its smell."

"No," I corrected him, "it's because when he laughs he giggles. I picked that up somewhere."

"Are you living in Paris?" he asked.

"No, I lost my passport."

"They'll issue you another."

"That wasn't how I lost it," I had to explain. "I meant they won't renew it."

"Why not?"

"They won't tell me why."

"The Shipley woman," Hemingway said, "she won't tell *anybody* why."

"I'd like to talk to her husband," I said.

"Help yourself," he suggested.

I did.

"Another big deal is the lioness," I reported, because I thought Hemingway ought to know. "The old man don't hunt. He has two old ladies in his stable he's pimping and just lays under a tree while they go out and run down an elk and drag it home. He won't even help drag. He just lays under that tree till his old lady comes back from the supermarket dragging the groceries. He don't even help drag. When dinner is over they move on so the hyenas can come up and crunch the bones."

There was a silence. Hemingway had run out of fighters and I'd nearly run out of hyenas.

"Another thing," I felt he ought to know, "if he catches you sleeping he'll bite off your face."

"Was *that* in the movie?" Hemingway asked quickly.

"No, I picked it up somewhere."

Hemingway got out of bed painfully. He was fully dressed. There were guests waiting.

He sat among them gravely serious. He carried an air of tranquillity. He didn't throw a punch at anybody. He didn't stagger. He didn't brag. He listened, perceived, and he liked having company. What he brought to a table of many guests was the feeling that everyone understood one another. I remember hearing Spanish spoken, and French, and of understanding not a word of what was said; and of knowing, when I spoke English, that some of the guests didn't understand me. But because of Hemingway's presence everything seemed understood.

I spent that afternoon and the next day, which was Christmas, with the Hemingways. He was a big man who had had a big life; that had made those who had known him bigger.

But they weren't going to give the money back in the mutuels.

*

Seven years later, cornered by death, a professor with a notebook came at him out of the shadows.

"He had read, or glanced at, I could soon see," the professor

reported, "not only my essays, but practically everything anyone had written on the modern novel in the United States.
I fancied Hemingway flipping the pages, checking the in-
dexes (or maybe he got it all out of the book reviews in *Time*),
searching out the most obscure references to himself, trying
to find the final word that would allay his fears about how
he stood; and discovering instead, imbedded in the praise
that could never quite appease his anguish, qualifications,
slights, downright condemnations... 'A whole lifetime of
achievement,' I wanted to shout at him, 'a whole lifetime of
praise, a whole lifetime of reveling in both. What do you
want?' "

For you to go away. Was that asking too much?

"Okay, so you've written those absurd and trivial pieces on
Spain and published them in *Life*," the professor wrote, "okay,
you've turned into the original old dog returning to his
vomit. We've had to come to terms with your weaknesses as
well as your even more disconcerting strengths—to know
where we are and who, where we go from here and who we'll
be when we get there."

("These damn students," Hemingway once complained,
"call me up in the middle of the night to get something to
hang on me so they can get a Ph.D.")

"Hemingway," the Ph.D. concluded, "sometimes puts down
the closest thing to silence attainable in words, but often what
he considers reticence is only the garrulousness of the inar-
ticulate."

There is a corruption of prose which is jargon.

Gentlemen, I give you jargon:

"Silence and platitude. Platitude and silence. This was the
pattern of what never became a conversation. And I felt, not
for the first time, how close Hemingway's prose style at its

36

best was to both; how it lived in the meagre area of speech between inarticulateness and banality: a triumph wrung from the slenderest literary means ever employed to contrive a great style—that great decadent style in which a debased American speech somehow survives itself."

This is jargon: its "Yes" is not "Yes"; its "No" is not "No." It is jargon because it diffuses meaning in order to conceal, rather than reveal, the writer's thought. It is jargon because it conveys the impression that the writer is employing Elegant English at the same time that it enables him to falsify his thought. It is jargon because it seeks to make an idea, that is easily refutable, irrefutable. Put into prose, the writer's thought here is that Hemingway was uniquely fortunate in having devised a great style while he had nothing to write about. Put thus honestly, the writer would appear asinine. Jargon, therefore, is the corruption of prose deriving from the writer's own corruption.

"But what were we doing talking of 'next books,'" the professor continues, "when I could not stop the screaming inside my head—'How will anyone ever know? How will I ever know unless the critics, foolish, biased, bored, tell me, tell us?' I could foresee the pain of reading the reviews of my first novel, just as I could feel Hemingway's pain reading the reviews of his later work. And I wanted to protest in the name of pain itself that not separated but joined us."

Had the man driven from Montana to Idaho to interview Hemingway or to present himself as a victim? Hemingway hadn't sent for him.

"But all the while he [Hemingway] kept watching me warily, a little accusingly."

Hemingway knew about lions and he knew about lionesses. He had been the man lying with blue wounds from elbow to wrist; he had been the English girl dreaming herself dead in an Italian rain. He had felt the wind of buzzard wings; and knew what it felt like to be an ex-fighter driving a cab. He had seen the elephant, he had seen the owl. He had smelled the hyena:

Highly humorous was the hyena, obscenely loping, full belly dragging at daylight on the plain, who, shot from the stern, skittered on into speed to tumble end over end. Mirth-provoking was the hyena that stopped out of range by an alkali lake to look back and, hit in the chest, went over on his back, his four feet and full belly in the air. Nothing could be more jolly than the hyena coming suddenly wedge-headed and stinking out of the grass by a donga, hit at ten yards, who raced his tail in narrowing scampering circles until he died.

Small wonder Hemingway kept watching warily.

The hyena, the classic hyena, that hit too far back while running circles madly, snapping and tearing at himself until he pulls his own intestines out, and then stands there jerking them out and eating them with relish.

"I stood for a moment," the interview concludes at last, "watching Hemingway banging at the closed doors, rather feebly but obviously tickled to be able to feel. 'Shit,' he said finally to the dark interior and the empty street; and we headed for our car fast, fast, hoping to close the scene on the first authentic Hemingway line of the morning. But we did not move quite fast enough, had to hear over the slamming of our car door the voice of Mrs. Hemingway calling to her husband, 'Don't forget your vitamin tablets, Daddy.' "

38

Hemingway knew the action:

—*Trailer of calving cows, ham-stringer, potential biter-off of your face at night while you slept, sad yowler, camp-follower, stinking, foul with jaws that crack the bones the lion leaves—*

the trip had been worthwhile.

June 29th: East China Sea: We Didn't Come to Gamble.

"I came to gamble" is the land-gambler's brag and *Deal* is his one command. Don't tell us about your love-life—*Deal*. While one deck is being dealt another is being shuffled so not a moment will be lost: all moments tonight are stolen from wife, children and home, we have to get in as much play as we can. And every deal seems slow.

Poker upon the roving deep isn't poker on dry land.

When goony-birds dip the deadly hours, pursuing, fleeing, again pursuing, the automatic foghorn mourns, the long deck tilts as the waters shift and the waters shift once more: then a rain-dashed fleck through an open port and the dealer lays down the deck.

Play stops. Talk stops. Even the engines below us wait; the port is closed.

Then like a great heart hauling hard, the engines begin to throb once more, the long deck tilts as the waters shift and the waters shift once more: the automatic foghorn mourns and the cards go around and around once more.

Seaman of The Republic, castoff care-nothing from suburb and slum, unschooled craftsman and long-schooled drunk, skilled mechanic sick of the land or drop-out dropping yet, under the moon of the East China Sea, with a pack of stained

41

NOTES FROM A SEA DIARY

cards on a green-baize board, all are now gathered together:

1. Crooked-Neck Smith, age 38, ordinary seaman who runs this seaman's game.

2. Bridelove, about 35, squat and dark as a piece of heavy machinery beveled to a precision function.

3. Muncie, 22. Bridelove tells him what to do.

4. Quong, Officers' pantryman, an ageless, small, immaculate Chinese enormously skilled in minding his own business.

5. Chips, Ship's carpenter, about 50. Thirty years of exposure to the suns of Southeast Asia have left him as pale, from the folds of his neck to the folds of his belly to the folds of his mind, as though he'd been living in a sanitarium.

6. Carey "Sparks" Concannon. A seventeen-year tour of the gin-mills of Asia has not sufficed to wash the dust out of the throat of this dust-bowl refugee.

7. A free-lance journalist out of Chicago.

Lowball is the game with these seaborne stiffs who settle for low in everything. Concannon appears to be the only one of the lot deeply dissatisfied with a life of many big drunks and few small cares, a pint of cheap gin and a girl by the clock; of being expendable at sea and unwanted on the beach; and of coming at last to fear any woman not for sale or rent.

Call *that* a life on the roving deep.

If your wife can't stand your moods any more, your girl friend claims she's broke, if you can't dance and can't stay sober, then a mariner's life, a seaman's life, a jolly life on the rolling deep, *that's* the life for you.

The Negro seaman's story is something else, of course: a way out of a slum with equal pay and a tour of ports where color don't matter.

"What. Kind. Work. You. Do. Mister?" Muncie asked me.

"I'm in iron and steel," I told him, "my wife irons and I steal."

42

Quong laughed. But, then, Quong laughs at everything.

"Quong," Concannon saw fit to put in, "here's a man *paying* to go to Calcutta—what do you think of *that?*"

"Oh-oh-oh—*Cay-O-Cutta,*" Quong recalled, *"Cay-O-Cutta* gel, she treat *him* very nice. Very pretty gel, he *glad* he come *Cay-O-Cutta.*"

"Wait," Bridelove tried to wise me up, "wait till you *see* Calcutta."

"Is it really that bad?"

"Wait," Bridelove reassured me.

"I. Don't. Like. Memphis," Muncie announced. Muncie didn't stutter. He just couldn't handle a whole sentence together.

"This boy ain't stupid," Bridelove assured me quickly, "just slightly retarded."

"Oh. No. I. Only. *Slow,*" Muncie explained.

Then the cards went around, the goony-birds dipped, the long deck tilted as the waters shifted.

"Seven-card stud," Concannon announced, "high-hand only," and gave the deck to Chips, beside me, to cut.

He dealt me two diamonds down and one up. I paid to stay in just to see what he had in mind. Two clubs fell. I would have dropped but for that interesting exhibition Sparks had given me. When the ten of diamonds fell I took another look at my hole cards: I lacked nothing but the queen of diamonds to have a straight flush, king high.

I centered my index finger dead-center on the back of my hole-cards.

O little queen dressed in faggoty pink—

I waited until the cards had been dealt around, face-down, before I peeked—*fall my way and we'll all be rich.*

Six of clubs.

Ouch.

43

Smith won the hand. When Chips threw in his cards I saw that his last card had been the queen of diamonds. Missed by one. And it had cost me sixty dollars out of a traveler's check for a hundred.

"Let me have what you can spare," Chips asked me when Smith gave me forty dollars in change. I had three hundred more in traveler's checks when I pushed the forty to Chips.

In the next few hours I had a pat flush, a pat full-house, trips back to back three times and two straights. Sometimes the card I signaled Sparks for came; sometimes it didn't. When it did it made no difference. Smith topped me every time.

"Toward morning the farmer gets lucky," he encouraged me when my last hundred-dollar check went into a pot. I was holding two pair, aces up and deuces, and the game was draw. I signaled Sparks for a third ace. I didn't get it. I got the third deuce. As a full-house it would have to do. I checked to Smith. He bet and I raised. I raised him back. He raised me.

I felt a sudden chill and merely called.

He had a full house with fours up.

"If you'd filled up with aces instead of deuces," he began to console me as he hauled in the pot—"If the rabbit had been carrying a gun he would have shot the ass off that hound," I reminded him.

"Yes," Sparks put in, looking too benign, "and if your ass was pointed—"

"*Deal, deal,*" I demanded irritably. Something had gone wrong on the *Malaysia Mail.*

Toward morning the farmer went broke.

"Deal me out," I told Smith, and went up to my stateroom to watch the goony-birds through the porthole.

I waited, when I heard Sparks come up, until he'd reached his shack. Then I followed him into it.

44

He already had his headphones on when I came in.

Beep-beep-jot-jot-beep-beep-beep.

I waited.

Jot-jit-beep-beep-jit-jot-beep.

I helped myself to his gin. He took the headphones off.

"How much did you go for?" he inquired.

"The roll."

"You can get it back."

"How?"

"Transistors. You can buy them for twenty apiece in Hongkong and get sixty for them in Bombay. A hundred bucks will get you three hundred."

"I don't have a hundred left."

He pulled out his wallet and clamped on his headphones. "Take two out of there," he told me.

I took it.

We were twenty-four hours from the Port of Pusan.

July 1st: 472 Cho-Ryang-Dong:
A Parlor Once Purple
Now Faded to Rose

It is evening in this fogbound warren above the East China Sea: that low-burning hour when the sourish-sweet tenement-supper smell of *kimchi,* cooking upstairs and down, pervades harbor, hall and street. I'm waiting for Concannon in front of the American Club. The only sound is a lone hound's hunger-howl up the green mountain: then his echo begins sliding down. Chew your own echo, hound: call *that* supper.

"Man, do you think I'm going bamboo?" is all I've heard from Concannon for days. He's putting in so much time on this bamboo problem he's keeping *me* from going bamboo.

A woman naked to her waist and breast-feeding an infant comes slogging through the rutted mud toting a bucket of suds in her free hand. She's wearing a G.I. fatigue cap and sandals chopped out of a tire. Her features are ravaged so delicately it looks like hunger has used a thin chisel to form them. Four thousand years looks down, from that ancestral mountain, upon a race of hardluck aristocrats toting buckets of slopwater.

Slopwater is by courtesy of the American mess hall, *chapeau* by the Quartermaster Corps. Shod by Firestone, employed by nobody, impregnation courtesy of the American P.X. You can get anything at the PX.

47

Homemade soap is stuffed into *Palmolive* wrappers here; something passing for candy is offered as *Baby Ruth;* and cigarette snipes are dressed in beat-up *Chesterfield* packs. Girls are permitted inside the Seamen's Club; but their pimps have to wait outside.

I'll only stand around pretending to be a spy fifteen minutes longer. If Concannon doesn't pick me up by then, he's finally gone bamboo.

Here comes an aging slicky-boy with a mug divided between a beetling scowl and a smile, sweet as apple pandowdy, under a frightwig of black-wire hair. How can a mug like this get himself a girl to work for him?

"Number-One Joe! Welcome Club Frisco!"

Pumping of my hand.

He looks like he's been creeping under a fence and part of the wire has stuck to his skull. One side of his face has been paralyzed and the other side survives only by that smile. Well, that's what comes of crawling under other people's barbed wire.

"Long time you gone, Number-One Joe!"

I feel like I've never been away.

"Make yourself home, Number-One Joe! What I got for *you! A*-One quality for Number-One Joe!"

The red, white and blue card he slipped into my hand framed an American sergeant embracing a slant-eyed girl under a palm. Slicky-Boy must have a Los Angeles Branch.

We have very nice girls and all kind of drinks—try onece, the card informed me.

"Waiting for friend," I explained, returning the card.

"*What* frien' *Who* frien' *Where* frien'? *You* come by Club Frisco, *me* Number-One Joe's good old frien'." He took my arm—a move to which I have an aversion as it makes me feel I'm being pinched. I shook him loose and he looked dum-

48

founded. How could I walk out on him after he'd been waiting for me so long?

"You *Captain*-Ship now or something, Joe?"

"No," I had to admit, "not Captain. Only passenger."

"Pass-in-*Chair!* O God!" He struck the back of his hand
to his forehead at the news. *"Now* you Pass-in-Chair! O, you
come longside *me,* Number-One Joe. Pass-in-Chair! I got for
you A-One Quality Eng-ilsh Pass-in-Chair-gel!" He took me
into custody again.

Again I uncustodified myself; and again he didn't like it.
He stepped in close and lowered his voice to a stoolie's
whisper.

"What you like, Joe?"

Talent can spring up anywhere.

"I like you go," I guarant*eed* him.

"You give dollar, I go," was his counter-offer, "far."

"Give nothing."

"No go far."

His breath was formidable. But if he could stand it all day
I could put up with it a few minutes.

Sparks was coming down the other side of the street with
his specs in his hand, blind as an owl. I cut over to meet him.

Slicky-Boy Number One, Port of Pusan, came up on Sparks'
other side. "Hi, Joe! Me your good old frien'!" Sparks adjusted his specs and looked down.

"Who's your buddy?" he asked me.

"I don't know," I replied, "but he's hard to shake."

Slicky-Boy followed us up to Kim's place, where Sparks
blocked him and slammed the door in his face.

He hadn't been hard to shake after all.

Up a narrow stair through a cloud of *kimchi*, past a furlong of doors, all closed. Then an open one and a high, flat
warning like a very old woman's cry—

49

"Number four-seven-two Cho-Ryang-Dong! Ryang-Dong! Ryang-Dong!"

It was a purple-black bird, no larger than a crow, perched in a cage big enough for a turkey. In a parlor from some age that was purple; that now had long faded to rose.

A great old-fashioned bed of the curtained kind, stood with its curtains drawn as though they'd been drawn for years. A portable record player and a few chairs: we were home.

"Ryang-Dong! Ryang-Dong!" the myna bird shrieked. *"Pay what you like!"*

A slant-eyed little fireship in a green kimono, her dark hair piled, came forward as softly as a Siamese cat. I saw why communications officers go bamboo.

"Him crazy," she nodded at the bird.

"Him not so crazy," I thought to myself.

"Meet Kim," Concannon decided to introduce me.

She gave me both hands so narrow, so firm; in her brief grip I felt a contained pride.

How many a midnight seaman, on leave or on the beach, had she locked fast between those slender thighs? And held till he'd fainted within her? Then had kicked him lightly in the small of the back with her childlike slipper—"Time up, Joe!"

And yet had kept her pride.

How many midnight passages with the robbed drunk sleeping it off and the desk clerk waiting below? How many madams? How many jails? How many slicky-boys? How many blows? Seamen on leave or on the beach, M.P., tourist, policeman and pimp, each had taken his measure of her flesh. Not one had let her go.

In bars where fists are what count most, chance had pitched her, small and weak. She'd made shore on her own strength alone.

50

"Me speak Eng-ilsh pretty good," Kim assured me, "but not read worth good damn"—she took a record off the player and put a finger on its title—"You tell, please."

The record was *Rock Love*, that I'd first heard in a Chicago bar nearly as old-fashioned as the parlor where I now stood, in 1953.

Kim stood over it as it played, guardedly. The machine was her most precious possession. Music that an American woman can buy for a dollar, she had had to pay for more dearly.

> *You got to have Rock Love*
> *Deep in your heart*

Concannon drew the bed-curtains aside and stretched out like a begoggled bear; the first low snore of Kingfisher (Oklahoma's) greatest lover, rumbled forth. Kim took my hand, led me to a window, raised the shade and pointed down.

"Port of Pusan," she explained.

A line of low roofs shimmered as though oiled; around a pond so stagnant that it gleamed. Thin trails of smoke rose from rooftops toward a moon so low it looked tethered.

"*Kimchi*," she told me, "are *cook*-ing."

The women of the shacks were cooking *kimchi*. A dog head-down and dreaming of dinner came trotting between the pond and the moon.

Kim raised the window and called, in a silvery twitter, to someone below.

A girl, wearing a babushka, stepped out of a door that sagged on a single hinge. She turned her face up to us and waved; then went back into her sag-door house. Kim drew the shade.

"Port of Pusan," she repeated sorrowfully.

> *So when temptation rocks moves your soul*
> *The rock of love won't let you roll—*

51

And seamen's voices in the street took up her sorrow, like voices trying to feel happy far from home. I had heard that lonesome pining in voices of farm-boys singing no farther away from home than their town's last street-lamp.

Concannon murmured in sleep. Kim unlaced his boots and took them off without waking him. Concannon wriggled his toes as though dreaming he was walking barefoot in the sand-hills again. Then turned on his side, cursing somebody—*"Ahr-ahr-your-ass-I'll take-ahr-ahr-arh-Ho-Phang Road—"* and into a dreaming triumph, I think, of pitching Manning over a rail into heavy seas.

Kim opened a brown paper bag and put it into the bird-cage: the bird backed into it.

A light warning tap at the backstair door, and in walked a robust, smiling child, to fling off her babushka with a smile so white it lit the dimness. She was wearing dark bangs and looked as though she had been in town just long enough to shake the rice out of her sandals.

"Po-Tin," Kim introduced her.

"Pass-in-Chair," she added.

Kim poured a shot of Scotch for me and another for Po-Tin. The country girl wrinkled her country nose: a mere nub of a nose as noses go.

"Wee-skee, no good," Po-Tin explained, *"Coca-cola, good."* Her breasts were so full that their nipples indented the thin cloth of her sweater. All she wore, it appeared, was the sweater, a blue-belted skirt of dark red, and sandals. She drew a small fan out of the belt and came to me, smiling self-consciously while spreading the fan. I took it from her and put it aside. It didn't fit either the scene or herself. On my lap she cocked her head.

"Pass-in-Chair?"—and glanced at Kim for enlightenment.

"Him not work longside ship. Him pay money for just ride.

52

Him sit in chair. Captain-Ship bring him *kimchi*," Kim explained authoritatively.

I finally got it: A passenger was one who passed over sea seated in a chair. Po-Tin studied me incredulously.

"You pay Captain-Ship for just *ride?*"

The American millionaire assented smugly.

She put an around my neck.

"You give Po-Tin much dollar?"

I held an American dime to the light, then put it between her breasts. Po-Tin giggled.

Then, lifting her arms above her head, she invited me to raise the sweater. It came off easily. The dime rolled onto the floor. Concannon's mug came through the curtains, his eyes filmed by sleep, struck out one paw and the dime rolled into it. It was like seeing an outfielder, blinded by sun, stick out his glove to let a line-drive smack into it.

The milky beauty on my lap felt no more self-consciousness about her breasts than she did about her ears. She poked a forefinger into my chest.

"Pass-in-Chair, you take Po-Tin longside ship? You take Po-Tin Ny-agara Fall by Cal-ifornia? Me cook for you. Me no make bad-business by Ny-agara Fall, Cal-ifornia."

Concannon reared, put on his specs, fixed his sightline and stared.

"Looks like we've *all* gone bamboo," he decided. And fell back to a snoring sleep with that dime still clutched in his paw.

> *When storm-winds blow and the waters shift*
> *The rock of love won't let you drift.*

From the depths of her green kimono, Kim brought up a narrow cigarette wrapped in brown paper and dragged on it deeply. Its odor, so poignant, flowered the dark and heavy air like a flurry of scented confetti. She passed it to Po-Tin.

53

Po-Tin put the stick to my lips; I closed my eyes and drew deep.

Nothing happened. Not a thing.

I turned it to Po-Tin's mouth and she dragged on it solemnly.

Her eyelids fluttered, as one viewing a more distant scene. Then a shutter fell across her vision. I took this phenomenal snipe from her lips and tried once again.

Nothing. Nothing *whatsoever*.

The girl against my chest let her arms drop loosely across my shoulders: my Smiling Child was stoned.

And her breath, that was sweet, fled across my cheek. And her breast swelled tight to the cup of my hand; like a small animal preparing itself for rest.

Girls, I thought, those with hair like light and those with hair darkly piled; girls, I thought, with smiles still expectant and those with no smile left at all; girls, I thought, whether in sleep or waking, lips parted in wonder or suddenly laughing: girls have a hard time of it everywhere.

The air grew weighted and all times felt troubled. For all ports with low-burning lights awaited a long ship low to the waters.

A long ship far out, moving without lights, through the fogs of the East China Sea: seeking its final dock. All voyages were now done.

All the lowball games at sea and all the poker hands had been played; at sea or on the beach. The gambler lay in the gambling-room. Cards were still scattered across the floor. The seaman slept beside his whore. The farm-child wakened beside its mother—and saw the lights of passing cars move across the ceiling.

Someone was standing on the other side of the door.

The room had gone cold, and the half-naked girl on my

lap was pressing against me for warmth. Someone kept trying the latch.

Someone is always trying the other side of somebody's door, I thought, slipping back into darkness and fog. Someone is always trying somebody's latch.

When I came awake, later, it was because Kim was rocking Po-Tin awake. The girl's head was lolling like a child's.

"Ny-agara Fall by Cal-ifornia," she murmured.

I put her on her feet, snatched Concannon's bottle and held her against me down the dark backstairs, following Kim with a flashlight.

Kim held us back at the door while she went out into the warren of *kimchi* shacks and clotheslines stretched across the moon. Po-Tin put her hand on the back of my neck, while we waited in the darkness, and pressed my nape. Her fingers were strong.

"Come," Kim told us.

Po-Tin led me by the hand. She walked under a clothesline without stooping—it caught me across my forehead and I stumbled across a sleeping hog; that grunted and ran away. The girl laughed softly in the *kimchi* gloom.

She lived in a little *kimchi* house with an earthen floor, where *kimchi* mice ran in and out in the light of a *kimchi* moon. Incense cut the odor of *kimchi* while she undressed in the dark.

Po-Tin stood by the window a moment in the light of Asia's moon; a girl all smoky gold with hair like the sleeping sea.

Then she came toward me.

When I wakened the moon had set. What was I doing in Asia?

Upon other wakenings far from home, in a tent pitched on a German racetrack, in the bow of a Greek fishing boat or on

55

NOTES FROM A SEA DIARY

a rooftop in Fez, I'd known what I was doing there. This time I could find no other reason than that I didn't want to be at home.

And what troubled Concannon so about going bamboo? What was wrong with bamboo-root for the man with no roots at all? I drew the sleeping girl to me. She pressed herself hard against me without waking. Her lips parted as her breath came harder, yet she didn't waken. Then took me in, so warm and so deep that I was glad I hadn't stayed at home.

I dreamt I was searching around a pond that was strangely still, for some flower that grows only under water. I was about to find it when I felt myself heaved bodily and wakened coming down on my face.

It was morning and Po-Tin was being playful. Naked as she had slept, she hurled herself like a small bear upon me. Despite a fifty-pound weight advantage, it was all I could do to keep from being pinned disgracefully. Yet, every time I squirmed out from under her, she butted me in the side.

Sensing my irritation at being unable to overpower her, she relaxed long enough to permit me to pin her. Then lay, smiling up, her long eyes glistening.

"What got into *you?*" I asked the little brute.

"I happy," she told me.

Well, what do you know.

Breakfast consisted of two cups of instant coffee, black. She was out of milk. She was out of sugar.

Orange juice: out. Cereal: out. Fried eggs with bacon curling: out. Toast, marmalade, wheatcakes, butter and cream: out.

Out like her checking account. Out like her social security. Out like her life insurance and her driver's license. Out like her electric lighting, her inside plumbing and running water; her morning paper and her diner's card. Out like her books, like her records; like her carpeting, curtains, music, and mail.

Lovely as she was by moonlight, I decided not to live with Po-Tin until the Westernization of Korea had gotten farther along.

The G.I. blanket under which we'd slept looked like it had been recaptured at Hill 29. A pair of G.I. combat boots, recently shined, stood in a corner. Somebody had been trying to reassemble a radio out of the parts of a half dozen shattered sets—and Po-Tin didn't seem to be mechanically inclined.

She clutched the ten-dollar bill I'd given her between her palms, in the manner of a child pleased at a gift yet secretly fearing it is going to be snatched away from her. I hoped Kim would catch her another trick before the tenner was gone.

"You come back, take me longside Ny-agara Fall, Cal-ifor-nia," she instructed me.

I poured a farewell shot of Concannon's Scotch.

"When I come back," I promised her.

I found my way across the slum where pigs slept below clotheslines and American tires, stripped of rubber, lay like ruined expatriates. Then, remembering I'd forgotten Concannon's bottle, cut back across the yard.

The door was shut. Po-Tin didn't answer my knock. I walked in all the same.

The bottle was on the table. Slicky-Boy sat on the edge of our bed smoothing my ten-spot across his knee. Po-Tin sat in a crashed-in heap at his feet, touching a dab of cotton to her mouth. Her lip had been split.

I snatched the ten-spot, wadded it, and flung it to a far corner of the room. Don't ask me why.

Slicky-Boy stared up with his jaw hanging. Then he looked down at his knee, where the bill had just been; and saw it wasn't there any more. Po-Tin scrambled across the floor on her hands and knees, snatched it and raced to Slicky-Boy with it; where she unwadded it across his knee.

There must be *some* way of getting out of this.

Slicky-Boy took the bottle from my hand, drank, and returned it to me.

"You got cigarette, Joe?" he asked.

He took the pack from my hand, extracted one; then pocketed the pack.

"Oh *man*," his heavy look warned me, "you *are so wrong.*"

Kim came in looking for Concannon's bottle, saw Po-Tin on the floor, and began giving Slicky-Boy holy hell.

I didn't know what she was saying, but it was plain she was cussing him out. She took the bottle from me, poured a drop on her handkerchief, dabbed Po-Tin's broken lip with it. Po-Tin made small peeping noises.

Suddenly, Slicky-Boy began dissenting from Kim's condemnation and pointing toward me.

"What's he saying?" I asked.

"You *Captain-Ship?*" she asked me.

"No," I told her.

"Him say? *Yes,* you *Captain*-Ship, take Po-Tin longside you by Ny-agara Fall, Cal-ifornia. He say you no take Po-Tin without you take he too."

"Okay, I'm the captain, and I'm not going to take either one."

Kim translated.

Slicky-Boy looked at me sullenly.

"You no Number-One, Joe," was his verdict—"you Number Six! Number Nine! Fourteen!"

And on that deadly insult I left.

Yet all across the littered slum I heard him crying derisively behind me—"Number-Nineteen—Joe! Twenty-Eight! Hey! Number-Sixty-Joe!"

I felt like Number-One-Hundred-Joe.

58

July 4th: East China Sea

"My head may be on sidewise," Smith was acknowledging some jibe without anger, "but it's got the best nose on it on *this* ship. How do you think I got to be a smeller for Some People's Gas if I couldn't smell gas where nobody else could?"

"One day you're an ex-fighter, the next you're an ex-smeller," I professed to be skeptical. He let his neck out one notch.

"As a matter of fact, in my case the two trades were directly connected, sir," he assured me—"it so happened in the army that a certain First Sergeant took such a dislike to me I couldn't get off K.P. So I beefed to the Battery Commander I was being taken advantage of. 'Have you done any fighting?' he asked me. I sensed he had something in mind. 'Not professionally, sir,' I told him, 'but I never minded hitting somebody with my fists if it was alright with the other fellow.' 'Would you like to try your hand at inter-battalion fighting?' he asked me. 'I'll go where I'm needed most, sir,' I answered promptly."

"How'd you make out?" I encouraged him.

"I won my first two fights on knockouts as they were both with fellows from California. Which came to me as a complete surprise, as I'd never been in a fight where I didn't get hit myself before. It dawned on me that I'd hit on a way of staying off K.P. as long as they didn't match me with anybody from outside of Los Angeles. As luck would have it, my third match was with a fellow from West Virginia. 'If you can hold him to a draw I'll see you make Pfc,' the Second Lieutenant promised me. 'What do I get if I decision him, sir?' I asked. 'Acting Corporal,' the man came through. I didn't dare ask what would happen if I knocked the fellow out—I didn't feel I was ready for a responsibility like *that*."

"What happened, Smith?"

"What happened when?" he regarded me absently.

"When you fought the fellow from West Virginia."

"O, *that*," he returned from whatever cloud he'd been on, "he broke my nose in the first round but I didn't know it till the bell rang for the last round. Then I sneezed and some fragments of bone blew out of my right ear. One hit the ref and he thought I'd done it a-purpose and give the West Virginia fellow the fight right there."

The story seemed to be over.

"What did that have to do with being a smeller for Some People's Gas?" I prodded him.

"O, that led directly *into* it. When I came up for discharge they told me I was entitled to a free operation so I would be able to breathe like a civilian, and the doc did such a good job, cleaning out my nose, that when I got back in civvies I found I could smell things I could never smell before—or that anybody else had ever smelled, for that matter. I could tell the smell of apples from the smell of pears from across the street of a vegetable store. I could smell the difference between a tomcat and his old lady. Put glue in a paste bottle and paste in a glue bottle and I could tell you you had those bottles mixed. I could smell things that you'd think didn't smell: Cardboard. Sawdust. Stamps. When I'd get on a street-car—*Wow!* People smell strongest of all. In bars I got so I

could tell whether it was Schlitz or Pabst in the schooner.
Once a bartender bet me I couldn't tell bourbon from sour
mash, and I won the bet—and one day—it was in the same
bar—I told him he had a gas leak. Nobody else could smell it
but me. I had to find it to prove myself, and I found it—his
refrigerator. He called Some People's Gas and the guy they
sent out couldn't smell it till I put his nose right *in* it. 'With
a nose like that you ought to be on my job,' he told me. 'How
much do you make?' I asked him. He got paid good. I went
down there and they put me on as an apprentice smeller. But
I rose through the ranks faster than I did in the army, and
didn't have to get into a ring with anybody from West Virginia neither. I was there six months when I had my big
success."

He was gone again, gazing at some far horizon through the
open port.

"You were saying you had a big success with Some People's
Gas," I reminded him when he looked ready to return.

"Why, the way it was with Some People's Gas was like this:
sometimes I had to crawl around a roof and sometimes I had
to crawl under the street. Sometimes I had to make a hole
in a floor and hang upside-down. Sometimes I had to scale a
wall and sometimes I had to fight off dogs. One night, toward
closing time, I was under a filling station looking for a screw-
driver I'd put down and couldn't locate, when I smelled gas.
It was a new station, using bottled gas, and the bottles weren't
leaking. I couldn't find the leak, but I reported it.

"Now, they got *Historians* at Some People's Gas that can't
smell bananas from noodle-soup, but they know every inch
of pipe ever laid down in Seattle, and they gave the report to
one of these Gasified Historians. He looked at his histories,
he studied all the maps, and the report came back: No gas

main ever laid in that area. 'That wasn't southern fried chicken I smelled,' I told them in the office.

"The next Sunday morning the apartment building next to the station blew up, with a wedding party going on on the third floor. The bride was blown to bits, the bridegroom was maimed for life, the best man had a leg blown off and one of the bridesmaids got her spine snapped in two.

"I owe it all to that army doctor who done such a good job operating on me. I give him full credit."

"You must have gotten a pretty good raise," I suggested.

Smith began to revolve his head gently, trying to decide whether I was serious.

"Not exactly," he told me, "I got fired the next week for intermeddling with Department of Gas Historians."

July 6th: South China Sea, Two Days from the Port of Hongkong. Dingding, Hinkletinkle, the Finkified Lasagna and the Man Too Timid to Damn.

I once went to New York for the skating at Rockefeller Plaza and was sharpening my skates when the telephone rang. A woman's voice, sounding like a cross between a crow's and a barbed-wire fence, informed me, "Alfred Bovine would like you for dinner."

"I don't blame him," I assured this charmer, and hung up. The phone rang right back.

"Don't you *like* lasagna?" the same voice inquired.

Realizing that Bovine had altered his plan of attack, I went down to the lobby with my skates under my arm.

They were waiting for me. I didn't place him right off, but he had the air of a pool-hustler who works days in an embalming parlor. He liked me too.

All the way to the restaurant they took turns recommending the lasagna.

"I'm a meat-eating mouse," I had to let them know.

We entered one of those Italian joints where all the waiters look like they want another crack at Ethiopia.

"Three orders of lasagna," Bovine decided.

"I'll eat anything that won't eat me," I corrected him, "but I draw the line at the cheese-and-flour route. Give me an oyster stew, filet mignon rare with several well-chosen champignons."

A lull like the grating of pebbles being dragged, against their common will, by an ebbing wave, ensued; yet the place was two miles from the sea.

"What do *you* do?" I asked the blonde just to see if she did anything but recommend lasagna.

"I work at Doubleday," she told me, "but I don't like it. Nobody laughs at Doubleday."

I could see how things might work out that way. "They laugh at Random," I assured her.

"I don't see anything funny in *that*," she assured me.

"I didn't think it was anything riotous myself," I had to admit. "I just thought it was better than sitting around looking at one another. After all, I'm not Zero Mostel."

"I wish you were," she told me.

"I wish you were Dorothy Loudon myself," I told her resignedly, "but there are people in hell who'd like ice-water too."

Bovine was chomping lasagna as though cheese were going out of style. If there was going to be any further conversation I'd have to make it. I'd finally placed him as a distributor of well-packaged precepts whom a friend of mine had once described as "too timid to damn and too stingy to applaud." But all that had been before my time.

"Have you seen any plays here?" he asked me. There was a dab of lasagna on his chin.

"I saw one about a fellow in jail," I recalled, "that reminded me of a fellow named Hinkle, who was once doing time in the machine shop at Jefferson City. He began eating bolts, nuts and washers with the notion that if he got enough metal inside himself he'd get sent to the dispensary. He got so much junk inside him that you could hear him tinkle when he walked, so the other cons called him Hinkletinkle. When they put him under the X-ray there was so much metal inside him they had to operate and the operation was a success."

"What is the point?" the lady inquired.

"Why, the operation was a success because the warden said 'We're transferring Hinkletinkle to the mental ward— 'mental,' not 'metal,' and I thought that was pretty good for a warden. Though I admit," I added hurriedly, "it isn't nearly as comical as the time when Judge J. Daniel Dingding tried a kid for getting out the hook-and-ladder on a false alarm."

"I'm doing a *critique* on Hemingway for *Commentary*," Bovine let me know. "Where are the *great* writers?"

"I read your papers on the Failure of Steinbeck, the Failure of Faulkner, the Failure of Fitzgerald, the Failure of Wolfe, and the Success of Irving Shulman," I filled him in. "I can hardly wait to read this one."

"All the great ones are gone," he mourned.

Somebody had put an oyster stew in front of me.

"There was this Chicago judge we called Dingding," I continued, "because once, long before he was elected to the bench, he'd turned in a false fire-alarm and gotten the hook-and-ladder dashing about looking for something on fire; only there wasn't anythng on fire. They couldn't do anything much about it except put him on probation and keep him away from matches because he was under-age. Dingding promised never to pull another firebox, and was so true to his word they made him a judge; and he has kept his word to this very day. To this day, if Dingding says he'll dismiss a case for five hundred dollars, he'll *dismiss* it."

"Your stew is getting cold," the lady told me.

"Wait till I finish the story," I promised her. "You'll howl. Because even though His Honor doesn't pull fireboxes any more, he still thinks like a man who'd like to own his very own hook-and-ladder—you ought to have heard him holler at this kid accused of setting fire to a school. 'We have to keep Chicago strong and America mighty! Bury this terrorist! Hard labor! No parole! Take him away!' But the kid jumped up and hollered as loud as Dingding, 'Your Honor! This case has been fixed'—and his lawyer jumped up and knocked the kid down right there in court!

" '*What* did he say?' Dingding asked the kid's lawyer.

" 'Your Honor, he said 'I'm only a kid from the sticks,' the lawyer answered as quick as that. Dingding looked at his bailiff and the bailiff gave Dingding a wink.

" 'In view of the defendant's extreme youth and it being a first offense we recommend mercy and suspend sentence until after lunch,' Dingding announced, 'go and sin no more.' "

"There's nothing funny in that either," the lady felt.

"But that isn't the end of the story," I explained to her, "because when the lawyer took this kid home and told his father what the kid had jumped up and said, the father knocked the kid down too."

"So?" she asked.

"So that same evening the bailiff dropped by and talked to the boy more like a father than the boy's own father.

" 'I feel so bitter about being knocked down in public,' the boy told the bailiff.

" 'Well,' the bailiff told him, 'we're in private now'—and knocked the kid down *again!*"

"Are you making this up as you go along?" she wanted to know.

"Well, Dingding came in later, wanting to know what the bailiff thought he was trying to get away with fixing a case behind his back, and the bailiff said he'd been afraid to mention it because he was afraid Dingding would be furious at the idea of fixing a case. 'I don't blame you,' Dingding acknowledged, 'I like a good thief—but a man who'd pull a fire-alarm in cold passion'—and he swung around and hit that poor kid so hard the kid went out cold right there on his own parlor floor."

"What *is* the point?" the lady demanded to know.

I looked at the last lonesome oyster in my stewless, drained and drying bowl. And the oyster looked back up as baffled as myself.

"The point is that, when it came *his* turn, Dingding hit the kid harder than anybody," I explained.

"What did you think of the play you saw?" Bovine asked.

"It was by an Irishman who'd spent eight years in an English prison," I recalled—"It was about Capital Punishment."

"O, this killing, killing, killing," Bovine grieved, "O Castro! Enough violence! Enough killing!"

"I just can't see how *anyone* can object to capital punishment for traitors," the lady sailed in.

"They used to hang eleven-year-olds for sheepstealing," I remembered reading, "but it didn't put a stop to sheepstealing."

"I wasn't talking about *stealing*," she corrected me, "I was talking about *treason*."

"A person's habits are pretty well formed by the time he's old enough to be a spy," I decided to go along with her, "now if they'd string up a couple of ten-year-olds for snitching as a preventive measure, it would put a short quick stop

67

to selling atomic secrets later. And there'd be more sheep for the rest of us. As it is there's hardly enough to go around."

Conversation somehow slowed down after that, being mostly about whether Theodore Dreiser was a Great *Great* Writer or just a pretty good old sport. I maintained that the pen is mightier than the sword.

Then, having disposed of the filet, I took a toothpick and began trying to pry my gums loose.

"Put that *away!*" the lady commanded me.

I'd *thought* that would get her.

I went to work so furiously that a fragment of filet pirouetted off the toothpick and taxied in on Bovine's spumoni. The lady was halfway to the door before, half into his coat, Bovine caught up with her. I had just time to grab my skates and catch up with them both as they went through the door, wedging the three of us tightly for one moment. Then the wedge broke, they fled into a waiting cab and wheeled off trailing a scent of finkified cheese.

A light snow was falling. I stood alone but for my toothpick and skates. Somewhere down on Sixth Avenue a siren wailed.

Making me wonder whether Dingding's disappointment wasn't the same as that of any critic, or critic's mistress, for whom all triumphant hook-and-ladders fade.

Until nothing is left along cold streets where nothing can ever catch fire again.

I understood why the critic preferred dead writers to living ones.

July 9th: Concannon Gets the Ship in Trouble or Assy-end Up on Ho-Phang Road

The blood on my shirt is not my own. It never worked for me. It was last employed by Manning. If he wants it back all he has to do is to wring out the shirt.

Manning won't be wringing anything out of anything until the swelling below his left eye subsides. Has anyone informed you that Communications Officers have *very* fast hands?

Traveler! You too can be the only man aboard sporting a Kowloon Shiner! A fast bust in the face, delivered with all the elements of total surprise, can be yours without provocation. Southeast Asia has the action because everybody coagulates faster there. Even children coagulate. Anything goes in a free-trade port.

Kowloon was the town for Japanese transistors and Ho-Phang Road was the street for lovely girls. We would find a bar leaping with merriment was THE PLAN: There Quong and I would wait while Concannon purchased transistors for one-third of what we would be able to sell them for in Bombay.

Time was of the essence. The *Malaysia Mail* would stand off Hongkong for four hours, including the minutes that would be taken by the ship's shore-launch. So Concannon asked the driver to put in at Kowloon when we boarded the launch. The motor was going when Manning climbed in. Nobody had sent for him: he just climbed in.

"We're not going to Hongkong," Concannon told him. "We're going to Kowloon."

Manning didn't reply. He just sat at the end of the launch by himself. It looked as if he had it in mind to follow us around Kowloon to see whether we were buying Japanese transistors.

Concannon was our leader. Transistors was our mission. Lovely girls would be our reward. But how was Quong, who sometimes took as long as half an hour to fall in love, going to find time to fall in love twice in Kowloon? If he didn't it would be the first port in which he would fall in love only once. Concannon, of course, held the ship's record by falling in love five times in two hours. But there was a fifteen-minute limit in that whorehouse.

"You don't have a wife in every port because you're a seaman," I reminded him, but he cut me short.

"You've used that bit before," he told me dryly.

When we stepped onto the Public Pier, the heat hit us straight out of the airless vault of a Chinese slum—and straight down into that vault we went.

Multitudes: multitudes: haulers of carts and bearers of water, bicyclists, pedicabs, taxis, drivers of jeeps, honking vendors of fish in a heat the hue of a yellow dream. Ho-Phang Road lay between tenement terraces festooned with clothes drying in the scorching air.

Concannon milled ahead of us. Sparks never picked a boulevard to stroll when there was an alley to prowl. He wasn't content simply to make his way somewhere—if he didn't have to force his way he was unsatisfied. We had to hurry to keep

70

the crown of his head, where the hair had thinned, in view. His object being to lose Manning, he dodged into a bar under a sign that said: *The Lion of Kowloon.*

A wave of cold air rushed over me as soon as the door shut behind me. After the murderous heat of the street, this air-conditioning felt like a plunge into a pool for seals. When the dimness lifted I looked around.

The whores of that cave were waxen horrors transfixed by times long gone. One Chinese hooker loomed so huge, flesh enfolding flesh, that her eyes began melting helplessly as her belly began to swell. Beside her sat one so gaunt that her shadow had bones. I felt the wind of a cold depravity.

A Japanese girl on a bar-stool in a bright dirndl, swung about darting her pink tongue-tip at me and then smilingly spread her legs. She wasn't more than sixteen and her dress was high on her black-mesh thighs. The Lion of Kowloon growled low. We took seats either side of her.

A Japanese seaman left a drink standing to come over, take the girl by her arm and lead her out. Protectiveness turns fast to love.

His move left the cave looking more like a wax museum than ever.

"This looks worse than Korea," I accused Quong, "you told me things were going to get better."

"Wait," Quong promised me.

"Wait for *what?*"

Quong, out of the memory of his seaborne years, began searching for some port where I would be happier.

"*Sitagong!*"—he hit on it—"*Ooo-ooo—* When you get to Sitagong! *Muts* better gel, Sitagong."

"*Really* better in Chittagong, Quong?"

"*Betta? Ooo-ooo!* Pretty gel come *get* you in Sitagong! Very-pretty Sitagong gel take you home! Sit on lap! Fan you! Kiss-kiss! *Ooo-ooo*—How pretty Sitagong gel kiss-kiss!"

How much is this going to cost me, Quong?" I inquired calmly.

"Cost you?" He looked at me incredulously. "Not cost *you.* Sitagong gel, she not *like* Pakistani man—*American man for Sitagong gel!"* He started swinging his right hand over his head as though he were pitching for a girl's indoor softball club; and a girl took the bar-stool next to mine as if she wanted to play catcher. Quong whispered into my ear, *"And* give you bath! Put you in perfume-bubboo! She get in perfume-bubboo *with* you!"

"Quong!" I tried to stop him by sternness. "You aren't expecting me to believe that this girl is going to get into the bath *with* me?"

"Sure!" he insisted. "Very pretty sixteen-year-old Sitagong gel, she get in, scrub back, you foat."

"I *float?"*

"Sure, when she hit you on head, you foat. Assy-end up you foat."

I got to my feet. "Why should she hit me on the head for God's sake?"

"Wha' *for?* For take you pants. For take you shoe. For take you money. Hit one time real good you foat down River Tsangpo." He threw back his head in a Chinese convulsion and almost fell off the bar-stool. "Assy-end up! Assy-end up in River Tsangpo!"

The humor of the Oriental is apparently based upon the superstition that, no matter how preposterous a premise, mere repetition entails comedy. Although I could visualize a corpse floating down the River Tsangpo I failed to see that it was funny if it were mine. Assy-end up indeed! I turned to face the girl who'd joined us.

"What the hell *you* laughing at?" I asked this fool.

"My name Suzi," was her stupid reply.

"Where you from?" I asked her magnanimously.

"Sumatra."

"Meet Suzi Sumatra," I introduced her to Quong, "Frank's sister."

Now, if any, was the moment for hilarity.

Nobody laughed.

"Buy Lady-Drink?" Suzi—she had eyes of taximeter brown —inquired.

"She wants you to buy her a drink," I assured Quong.

"Lady-Drink," Suzi insisted. And what do you know, the bartender already had it poured!

I tasted it. Suzi drank it. Quong paid for it. It was my turn to buy.

"Short-term?" Suzi asked, "long-term?"

"This girl has fallen in love with you," I assured Quong, and left the pair of them to make a closer inspection of the whores of Ho-Phang Road.

One woman was so thin I paused to see whether she was a vertebrate. She thought I was flirting but all I was doing was trying to see whether she was held together by wire or string.

Lashes by *Maybelline,* talc by *PX—Even in the dark you know.* She wore one earring of amber and one of jade. Those things have a way of working loose in bed. Then you try to match one of each as best you can. For a ghost she had attractive cheekbones.

"Me Alina," she told me so tenderly that I decided to buy her a drink if she could swallow. "Two beers," I instructed the waiter.

"Wee-skee," my tender ghost corrected me.

73

I looked for marks on her arms but she didn't have veins. We went to a table. Quong and Suzi left to find short-term happiness.

What I found so winning about Alina was her combination of unearthly reflexes with a deathlike pallor. "Must be on muggles," I thought. But where could she hide a pipe beneath her dress without poking out some honest seaman's eye? If she weren't sniffing cocaine she must be taking heroin in her earlobes. It would have been nice to have found an opium-eater; but old-fashioned girls are hard to find.

Yet it has to be admitted that Kleenex, flesh-colored talcum and sixteen-gauge hypodermic needles have improved hygiene in free-trade ports. A girl who used to have to sneak down to a dirty opium pad at risk of her social standing, can now carry a sixteen-gauge hypodermic needle manufactured in New Jersey, in tissue manufactured in Ohio, and keep herself presentable on heroin brought in by American seamen. The exchanging of the poppy for the hype has brought the Orient closer to the Free World. More than one opium den has been swept out and now boasts a neon sign, saying MOM'S GOOD EATS; where you can get anything from redbirds to yellow jackets.

"Me Nepal gel," my ghost informed me. I had to keep an eye on the door for Concannon.

"Nepal gel very strong," she added, "make good pong-pong."

"You don't look too strong," I had to tell her.

"In Nepal me no make The Bad Busyness," Alina explained, "Bad Busyness no good for Nepal gel."

"How long you do Bad Busyness?" I asked just to get a line on her age. She looked so young yet so old.

She studied her fingers and finally held up two: "By Railroad Station, Madras, two year." She held up another: "By

Suklaji Street, Bombay, one year. Me get sick, go home Nepal, one year." Now all she had left was one thumb.

"You tell," she asked me, "in your country, do priest kiss priest?"

"Why do you ask *that?*" was all I could think to answer.

She took it for confirmation of what must have been an old suspicion. "My country best," she decided, "there we don't know *anything*."

When who walks through the door but The Unacknowledged Champion of Everything, Ship's Fink W. McAdoo Manning. And headed right for our table.

"Meet Miss Sumatra," I invited him.

Nobody laughed again.

"The ship-launch leaves in an hour," Manning informed me. "I just wanted to check it out with you."

He just wanted to get me out of the Lion of Kowloon, that was all.

"I'm waiting for the radio officer," I explained.

"Do you consider *him* reliable?" he asked me at the precise moment that Concannon, loaded with boxes, bottles and bags, loomed in the doorway.

"*Very* reliable," I told Manning.

Concannon began ambling about in the dimness—his eyes were weak even in the light of day. I guided him to our table. Manning waited until Concannon had dumped his packages on the table. I knew he hadn't yet seen Manning.

Suzi and Quong returned. That had been *really* short-term.

"*Loot!*" Alina cried happily. "*Loot! Loot!*"

"You're going to get the ship in trouble, Concannon," Manning spoke at last.

Concannon surveyed him without surprise.

"Are you coming?" Manning asked me sternly. He couldn't get over the idea that I was his charge.

75

I didn't answer. Yet he waited.

Sparks embraced both girls and kissed each in turn. Revulsion shadowed Manning's face like a wind rippling water. Why didn't the man leave?

A waiter came whizzing around the bar with a tray of drinks. Alina poured the gin.

Concannon extracted a transistor from one of the boxes, pulled out the aerial, and a hillbilly voice came droning in from some army base—

> All the good times are past 'n gone
> All the good times are o'er

Manning left in a high-wheeled huff. He actually thought the good times were o'er.

Concannon didn't think so. The whores of Ho-Phang Road didn't seem to think so. I'm sure *I* didn't think so. Alina sat on my lap.

"You look out," Quong told me, smiling his everlasting smile, "you not wait to foat in River Tsangpo—you foat *here*."

I didn't know what Quong was driving at.

"He means the slouch at the bar," Concannon informed me casually, "that's *his* old lady on your lap."

The Slouch, across Alina's shoulder, looked like one of those men so ineffectual you think he's English until his accent sounds Greek; and sure enough, he turns out to be Italian. I rotated Alina's skull toward him.

"Who *him?*" I inquired fluently, and unrotated the head. She giggled Chineasily.

"Him nutty-nut," she told me. The Slouch came over with a slouching motion.

"I am *sea*-man," he told us, and we had to take his word even though he looked like he'd been putting in more time

76

trailing John Gielgud than swabbing decks. Nonetheless I asked him to sit down and nonetheless he coldly declined. It wasn't, apparently, roaring good fellowship he was after in the Lion of Kowloon.

"May I have con-were-sation?" he requested me politely—putting this down with an injured air.

"Sure," I let him know.

"*Private* con-were-sation, if you please," he asked me.

I put Alina down and followed The Slouch into a stock-room back of the bar. I let him slouch in first. It was dark in there.

I followed.

"A am not *offended*," he assured me, "I wish all Americans to have joyous time."

I'll just bet you do.

"Good time, happy time"—and he gave me his hand as though he'd completed his message. Then he choked up, twitched, clasped his hands and unclasped them.

"My fiancée," he finally came out with it, "*good* woo-min."

"*Alina?*" I asked. "You wish me to enjoy myself but *not* with Alina?"

That I'd gotten the message relieved him; while his admission of jealousy left him more miserable than ever.

I didn't tell him that I'd invited her to have a drink only because I feel sorry for ghosts in need of somebody to haunt. I'd had no idea she was haunting *him*. He held my arm.

"A *great* woo-min!" He dropped his voice to a confidential whisper—"*Do not offer her money—you will only wound her feelings.*"

By making a determined effort, I felt I could suppress the impulse to hand Alina my wallet and watch. My lust for his hipless, breastless, stenciled, penciled, pseudo-Caucasian heroin-head was also governable.

"Our ship leaves in an hour," I informed him, putting my hand on his shoulder reassuringly, "may the shoes never be made that'll walk over your grave."

"The past is done," he announced as if, were it not for him, it would still be here. "What she once was she no longer is!" If it was Alina he was talking about that was a change for the worse, it seemed to me.

We returned to our table linked arm in arm.

"Wh*ee*-sk*ee!*" he demanded loudly, "wh*ee*-sk*ee!*" and a waiter came whizzing with a bottle and glasses.

"To Alina!" The Slouch raised his glass, and we all raised ours but Alina.

"Me no drink longside nutty-nut," she told us.

"He's jealous of you," I urged her, "he wants to marry you."

The thin crimson line of Alina's lips broke into a grin. Her teeth had gone bad.

"*Me* no marry nutty-nut. *Him* no give Alina money. Him all the time say *pong-pong, pong-pong*—but him no pay one goddamn dollar! Me say, 'Go longside ship, nutty-nut, I make *busyness'*—him say 'love, *pong-pong*, love, *pong-pong*' "—she threw a slanty glance at him with sufficient fury—then drank to him all the same.

Concannon began heaping the packages. We had just time to make the ship.

The Slouch liked the idea of our leaving so much he helped to speed us to the dock. When Alina picked up a shopping bag, he took its other handle. He wanted to be certain we wouldn't abduct her.

This pair were leading the loot parade, Concannon toting the gin, Quong the Scotch and Suzi and I bringing up the rear with the transistors, when the door opened from the outside and here was Manning blocking our way again.

78

"I *can't* let you get the ship in trouble, Concannon," he announced.

Concannon put his bottles down and, with ominous care, rested his hands on Manning's shoulders.

"*That* won't do you any good," Manning assured him confidently.

Concannon spun him aside, picked up the bottles, and again led us forth. It *had* done some good after all.

"The old man is going to hear about this!" Manning warned us. "This isn't the end of this!"

We fell inside the cab every which way. I had Alina on my lap and Concannon had Suzi Sumatra upon his and Quong was sitting on somebody that couldn't be anybody but The Slouch.

"To the docks!" our leader ordered and toward the docks we wheeled.

"*Looooot!*" my mascaraed ghost cried out, her head poking out of the window to the throngs of Ho-Phang Road— "*Looooot! Looooot!*"—while The Slouch fingered the hem of her skirt secretly, poor slouch.

"I hope the sonofabitch misses the ship," was Concannon's only reference to the purser we'd left behind us.

Riksha and trolley, bus and jeep swerved, skidded and reeled, beggars fled and an American seaman threw beer cans at us. "*Big fis' in river!*" Quong threatened him. A policeman whistled, fire broke out in a tenement and a Chinese child waved goodbye to us with a blue balloon.

Goodbye to the girls of Ho-Phang Road, goodbye to all wives left on the beach, goodbye to all Slouches madly in love and all Americans gone bamboo. Goodbye to Hum Hong Bay and the Chinese Y.M.C.A., the Kowloon Cricket Club and the Yaumati Vehicular Ferry. Goodbye to ancestral Kowloon and farewell to old Hongkong. I'm glad I saw your waxen whores may I never see them again.

The shore-launch was rocking at the dock. Suzi and Alina rushed the bags into the launch—and then sat down for the shore-to-ship ride. The Slouch tried to climb in beside Alina.

"Nutty-nut go home!" Alina cried out, so I shoved him back onto the dock—now here comes Manning breathing hard. As he clambered in he took command.

"Let's *go!*" he demanded of the driver—yet the driver wouldn't go.

"Letty go!" Quong commanded him too.

Yet he wouldn't go.

"What's he waiting for?" Concannon asked.

"He wants pay," Quong explained.

"Company pays for ship-to-shore transportation," Concannon remembered.

"The company launch went to Hongkong," Manning reminded us, "you went to Kowloon."

Manning was right. Manning was *always* right. I paid the driver.

"You fuckin' purser," Concannon told Manning.

"Nobody calls *me* a fuckin'—" Manning began and Concannon hooked a short right to his face. Instead of pulling back, Manning doubled forward with his forearms across his head, leaving himself wide open. Concannon slammed his left into the stomach and Manning went face-down, his arms still quaintly protecting his ears. Bottom up and face bleeding onto the boards, Manning looked like a fish whose gills have been ripped.

Concannon began kicking.

Alina came at him with her spindling arms straight out, her face still a mask—the boat lurched and Concannon teetered.

80

I got between him and Manning.

"You won," I announced. "See?" I asked Suzi and Quong, "*See?* Sparks won!"

Suzi turned her face toward the dock as though regretting having left it. Quong looked solemn.

"*You* stay out of this," Concannon warned me. He was hot, but he couldn't get at me because of Alina kneeling, in front of him, beside Manning. She gave Manning a handkerchief to hold to his face and had gotten him into a half-sitting position before Quong and I had the sense to see he was too heavy for her. We got him to the end of the boat and let him sit with his face toward the water. Alina held his head so he could throw up. Then she cleaned his mouth with her scarf and threw it over the side.

She sat beside him, protectively, until we hove to the *Malaysia Mail.*

Captain Karensen was hunched over the rail so mad he could spit: had it not been for not having anyone to replace Concannon he would have been gone half an hour. We let Manning get up first. He climbed painfully. I let Sparks go up right behind him in case Manning should fall. Quong scrambled up after Concannon. Not one of these fools remembered our loot. Karensen didn't look ready to delay his sailing hour in the interest of our black-market investment. I heard the anchor being raised.

I shoved one transistor under my belt and got one under either arm. The hell with the booze. "You take," I told Alina what to do with the rest of the loot. How a man could climb a two-story rope ladder with only teeth and fingertips I hadn't figured out, yet I made it all the same. Bridelove and Muncie helped me over the rail.

Manning was stretched on the deck. That had been a perfectly dandy shot to the stomach and a fairly good kick in the

NOTES FROM A SEA DIARY

eye. It had started to bleed again. Well, that's what comes of mixing with foreigners.

Bridelove, Muncie, Smith, Danielsen and Chips were more interested in my shirt than Manning.

"Wash it out with lukewarm water," Chips advised, "hot water'll shrink it."

When I looked at my bloodied shirt I understood: they assumed by it that it was myself who'd whipped Manning.

"How'd it start?" Bridelove asked.

"Ask Sparks," I suggested.

The launch below was wheeling about. Alina was at the rail no larger than a child, looking up. Only the mascara shadowing her eyes showed it wasn't a child's small face.

I waved, but she didn't wave back. Just stood looking up while I looked down; until I could no longer see her face.

Her face so young yet so old.

*

Manning opened the store for an hour that night just for the honor of the thing. But he was wearing dark glasses.

I didn't ask him how he was feeling. I went down to see whether the crew had any questions they might care to ask.

Smith was at his green-baize board, sitting slantwise to favor a boil he'd been developing on his behind, and shuffling a deck, but he had no players. A few seamen were sitting around, but none expressed curiosity about my bloodied shirt: my moment of glory, that had struck so brilliantly, had been too brief.

"Believe me when I tell you," Smith began, "the Marquis of Kingsbury, you can have him. Did you know his own son whipped him? I'm glad he did. I wish I'd whipped him myself. I could have, too. I beat better men than the Marquis of Kingsbury."

82

It wasn't easy to visualize Smith, with his jaw jutting upward from a neck fixed at angle, maneuvering an opponent around a ring.

"Did the bob-and-weave type of opponent ever give you any trouble, Smith?" I inquired tactfully.

Smith stopped shuffling. "What you're trying to ask is how could a man with his neck on one side be a fighter," he read me—"I took it up after my career as a gas-smeller was ended. In fact I contracted this hitch from such a terrible blow in the Adam's apple that it ruint *another* highly promising career."

"Were you *really* any good, Smith?" I asked.

"To tell you the truth, no, sir, I wasn't," Smith admitted. "But I *did* have color."

"How do you mean?" I wanted to know.

"Well one thing I done was I always wore a cap with the peak over my eyes into the ring. It worried my opponent not to see my face. I'd keep it on till the ref made me take it off just before the bell. Once a ref forgot and I had it so low I couldn't see my opponent and he knocked me cold. After that I just depended on my natural skills of which I had only two."

"Which two were they?" I asked to be obliging.

"One was how I never threw a low punch without following through with a fair one—they can't take a knockout back, can they? No fight crowd would stand for a referee doing that even if he could. This also had the effect of making the fight look to be on the level. My other thing was how I never pulled my head back when I butted, so's I wouldn't get butted back."

I waited.

"Once I was fighting a fellow with a skinny neck. He hit me low right off and, when I held, he hit me a short one in

83

my neck. At the bell he had his entire glove in my eye. So I dropped my hands and he hit me a clean shot that nearly took my head off. I realized then he had the referee so I didn't foul him back—I was afraid the ref would take the round away from me. And I didn't want to lose because I wanted to buy a Chevrolet. I had to beat him fighting fair or lose the Chevvy.

"When he came out for the second round he made as though to touch my gloves but I didn't accept his offer. So he bent me over a ring-post and laid his full weight on me till I thought my spine would crack before his referee took him off. Then he banged both my ears at the same time and backed off with his gloves up as if he had just been *boxing* somebody.

"I looked at the referee for help and that was another mistake, because this fellow immediately punched me in the neck again. It was the second fair punch of the fight and he had thrown both.

"Wouldn't you think the crowd would be proud of him for throwing two fair punches? They weren't. They booed. They thought punching a man in the neck was a foul. 'If he hits me in the neck a couple more times,' I thought, 'maybe the referee will take the round away from him.' When I went back to my corner I knew I would never be able to finish on my feet. So I said 'Goodbye Chevrolet.'

"I went out head down and butted him in the stomach. He went '*Oof.*' I brought my skull up against his right eye. He went '*Jzzz.*' Then I got my left glove around *his* neck. It was so skinny I could feel his windpipe through my glove. While he was choking to death I stepped on his foot. 'How does it feel?' I asked him. 'I'm disappointed in you,' he told me. My butt hadn't opened his eye so I dragged my laces across it and it opened fine. The referee noticed I'd changed my style. 'If you boys want to fight like this it's all right with me,' he told us.

"I pulled up my trunks and went to work. I butted him again and said, 'O, Pardon Me.' I scraped his back against the rope and said, 'O, Pardon Me.' 'Stop saying "O, Pardon Me," ' this fellow told me, and chopped me in the neck so hard I felt something come loose, so I drove my left five inches into his groin and I guess it must have stung him because he didn't express disappointment. He just doubled over like he was looking for something. I straightened him up with an elbow and hooked a *clean* left to his jaw. It was the fairest, cleanest punch I ever threw in my whole life. He went out like a light.

"But that referee! It took him eighteen seconds to count to six. He gave him six more to get to the count of eight. If he gave the man another half-minute it looked like he might get up. In fact, he rolled over at the count of ten. I held up my own hand before the ref could call it a draw. Then I went back to my corner and put on my cap and—"

"*Hold* it," I interrupted him, "hold it right *there,* buddy. You didn't go to your corner until the man was counted out? *No* referee, *nowhere,* ever started a count until a man got back to his own corner."

I had Smith cold.

"Sir," he reproached me gently, "when I told you I came into that ring wearing a cap I assumed you understood we weren't fighting according to the Marquis of Kingsbury. How could I have won by holding up my own hand if we're going by the rules? But you know—" he resumed quickly—"that fellow took so long to come to, that by the time he got back to his corner his handlers had left? That poor guy had to carry his own bucket all the way back to his dressing room. Nobody in that whole house offered him a hand. Isn't that a *shame,* sir?"

85

"It wasn't the Marquis of Kingsbury," I answered irritably, "it was the Marquis of Queensbury."

"Thank you," Smith answered, "I stand corrected. My point was simply that, whoever he was, you could have him. The reason he made up a set of rules about fighting fair was to cover up ways of fighting dirty. If he wasn't a dirty guy why did his son wait till he had him on the street to whip him, where the people could see? Why didn't he take the old man on at home? Believe me when I tell you, the Marquis of Kingsbury, you could have him."

"Let me ask you something else, Smith," I told him. "When a sailor dies at sea and is sewn up for sea-burial, does the last stitch go through his nose?"

"That's right," Smith assured me, "an old sea-tradition."

"*Why?*"

Smith studied me. When he studied you he rotated his head gently before reaching his decision.

"I'd like very much to fill you in on this, sir," he decided at last, "but the way I look at it is that any man who knows that the Marquis of Kingsbury was really the Marquis of Queensbury knows all there is to know. So what would an ignorant seaman like myself be doing trying to fill him in?"

He began dealing himself a hand of solitaire.

Sailors are a touchy lot.

July 13th: Indian Ocean: "I Can See You Have Been Wounded"

Had Jeannie With the Light Brown Hair died the same day as Ernest Hemingway, it would have been difficult to distinguish her work from his by some of the summaries.

"Hemingway's prose was as chaste as a mountain stream," one Magoo claimed of a stream bearing mules with their forelegs broken, stiffs floating bottoms-up and the results of several abortions.

"He was dedicated to Truth and Beauty," another mad groundskeeper claimed of a man who had always disposed of both abstractions in his "built-in shockproof shit-detector," as he described it.

The overpraisers were judges as useless after his death as had been the begrudgers before. Of whom one, describing a critical anthology about Hemingway, wrote: "He is still a sacred cow, and readers will look in vain through these pages for any sustained and fundamental attack on the American master. This must be accounted a reverential weakness in the editor's principles of selection. True we are given Barea's notable assault on *For Whom the Bell Tolls*—but this is an attack on only one book and only from one angle. The total considered rejection will not be found in these pages."

87

I hadn't known of Barea's notable attack. Indeed, I hadn't even known Barea was sick. Yet the reviewer's own affliction is plainly the same as that of the man who once explained to me why he opposed equality of opportunity for Negroes—"God-*damn* it, I feel inferior enough already!" It wasn't Hemingway's prose, but his life, which demanded "total and considered rejection." It wasn't his economy of language which made them feel small—it was his free-handedness. To men whose self-doubt put them in need of formal respect from others, the ease with which Hemingway earned the informal respect of workaday men and women felt like an accusation. It certainly never ceased to raise the hackles of such a domesticated peacock as Dwight Macdonald. Macdonald couldn't even bear Hemingway's beard.

"He was a big man with a bushy beard," * Macdonald wrote upon Hemingway's death, "and everybody knew him. The tourists knew him and the bartenders knew him and the critics knew him too. He enjoyed being recognized by the tourists and he liked the bartenders but he never liked the critics very much. He thought they had his number. Some of them did. The hell with them. He smiled a lot and it should have been a good smile, he was so big and bearded and famous, but it was not a good smile. It was a smile that was uneasy about the edges as if he were not sure he deserved to be quite as famous as he was famous.

"He liked being a celebrity and he liked celebrities. At first it was Sherwood Anderson and Ezra Pound and Gertrude Stein. He was an athletic young man from Oak Park, Illinois, who wanted to write and he made friends with them. He was always good at making friends with celebrities. They taught him about style. Especially Gertrude Stein. The short words,

* © Copyright 1962 by Dwight Macdonald. Reprinted from *Against the American Grain* by Dwight Macdonald by permission of Random House, Inc.

the declarative sentences, the repetition, the beautiful absence of subordinate clauses. He always worked close to the bull in his writing. In more senses than one, *señor*. It was a kind of inspired babytalk when he was going good. When he was not going good it was just babytalk. Or so the critics said and the hell with them. Most of the tricks were good tricks and they worked fine for a while especially in the short stories. Ernest was fast and stylish in the hundred-yard-dash but he didn't have the wind for the long stuff. Later on the tricks did not look so good. They were the same tricks but they were not fresh any more and nothing is worse than a trick that has gone stale. He knew this but he couldn't invent any new tricks. It was a great pity and one of the many things in life you can't do anything about. Maybe that was why his smile was not a good smile.

"After 1930 he just didn't have it any more. His legs began to go and his syntax became boring and the critics began to ask why he didn't put in a few more subordinate clauses just to make it look good. But the bartenders still liked him and the tourists liked him too. He got more and more famous and the big picture magazines photographed him shooting a lion and catching a tuna and interviewing Spanish Republican militiamen and fraternizing with bullfighters and helping liberate Paris and always smiling bushily and his stuff got worse and worse. Hemingway the writer was running out of gas but no one noticed it because Mr. Hemingway the writer was such good copy. It was all very American and in 1954 they gave him the Nobel Prize and it wasn't just America any more. Hemingway's importance is almost entirely that of a stylistic innovator."

Style is that force by which a man becomes what he most needs to become. When this need is one common to multitudes and the man's force suffices, we call him an artist, because in saving himself he saves others.

Ernest Hemingway's need was not to write declarative sentences with a beautiful absence of subordinate clauses. It was not to meet celebrities: he was on speaking terms with Georges Clemenceau, Benito Mussolini and Mustapha Kemal before he had heard of Ezra Pound and Gertrude Stein. He was one of the most highly paid correspondents in Europe.

Therefore the man had at his disposal a lifetime of meeting celebrities, while living comfortably with his wife and children in the capitals of the world; enjoying that degree of fame a foreign correspondent earns.

It was a lucky way of living—but he didn't want it. He didn't want it because, to him, it wasn't living at all. To Dwight Macdonald it would have been living. To have a respectable name with the Establishment and be a dissenter too! What *more* could a man ask than to have it both ways?

Hemingway didn't care for it either way. He wasn't an athletic young man from Oak Park. He was a soldier whose life had been broken in two. He didn't come to The Moveable Feast as to a picnic begun in Kansas City now being continued in the Bois de Boulogne. He had seen the faces of calm daylight looking ashen as faces in a bombardment. He had been the man who did not know where he went each night nor what was the peril there; nor why he should waken in a sweat more frightened than he'd been in the bombardment:

"But I must insist that you will never gather a sufficient supply of these insects for a day's fishing by pursuing them with your hands or trying to hit them with a bat ... Gentlemen, either you must govern or you must be governed. That is all, gentlemen. Good-day."

"I can see you have been wounded," the adjutant said.

90

Hemingway had felt his life fluttered like a pocket-hand-kerchief by the wind of death. In the watches of the night he had heard retreat beaten. Out of dreams like Dostoevsky's, endured in nights wherein he had lost his life yet had not died. Hemingway forged an ancestral wisdom in terms usable by modern man: that he who gains his life shall lose it and he who loses it shall save it; into a prose magically woven between sleep and waking.

Those were the nights the river ran so much wider and stiller than it should and outside of Fossalta there was a low house painted yellow with willows all around it and a low stable and there was a canal, and he had been there a thousand times and never seen it, but it was there every night as plain as the hill, only it frightened him. That house meant more than anything and every night he had it. That was what he needed but it frightened him especially when the boat lay there quietly in the willows on the canal, but the banks weren't like this river.

"Life is everywhere life," Dostoevsky had written after hearing himself sentenced to hard labor. "I am not dismayed. Life is in ourselves, not in outward things. There will be people beside me, and to be a *man* among men, and remain a man forever, not to falter nor fail in any misfortune whatever—that is what life is, that is where its task lies." Like Dostoevsky, Hemingway was a moralist whose waking resolutions were drawn from nocturnal visions. And in this he is much closer to the writers of the American twilight—Hawthorne and Poe—than he is to the image of the blood-and-guts adventurer that he projected—and *Life* swallowed whole.

"The critics had his number," Macdonald wrote. But it was Hemingway who had the critics', and particularly Macdonald's, number. Because Macdonald, who apparently has never read anything of Hemingway unless *Life* printed it, fell for the myth that Hemingway was a reporter of the bull-ring, the fight-ring, warfare, fishing and safari expeditions, but no more. Yet he was much more. Otherwise how explain these death-drawn visions?

> *They shot the six cabinet ministers at half-past six in the morning against the wall of a hospital. There were pools of water in the courtyard. One of the ministers was sick with typhoid. Two soldiers carried him downstairs and out into the rain. They tried to hold him up against the wall but he sat down in a puddle of water. The other five stood very quietly against the wall. Finally the officers told the soldiers it was no good trying to make him stand up. When they fired the first volley he was sitting down in the water with his head on his knees.*

Hemingway only began to write like this after he had learned how to sleep again. His life that had been broken in two, had healed strangely. As though his hold on life, having been loosened, now took a grip that possessed iron control. And from it derived a tension that fixed scenes dead-still as in dreams—yet that flowed with a secret life of their own:

> *Jack's sitting on the chair. I've got his gloves off and he's holding himself in down there with both hands. When he's got something supporting it his face doesn't look so bad.*
> *"Go over and say you're sorry," John says in his ear, "it'll look good."*
> *Jack stands up and the sweat comes out all over his face. I put the bathrobe around him and he holds himself in with one hand under the bathrobe and goes across the ring. They've picked Walcott up and they're working on him.*

92

Indian Ocean: "I Can See You Have Been Wounded"

There's a lot of people in Walcott's corner. Nobody speaks to Jack. He leans over Walcott.

"I'm sorry," Jack says, "I didn't mean to foul you."

"Memory remains," Dostoevsky wrote, "and the images I had created but not yet clothed with flesh. These will rend me to pieces, true, but my heart is left to me."

This conviction, so close to Hemingway's own resolve, explains why he had no more need of being a professional dissenter than he had for ingratiating himself with the powers that be. It wasn't his syntax, but the man inside the prose, that makes Macdonald struggle and fret to secure a hold on the man. For, to one so devoid of inner sinew as Macdonald, literature is explainable only in terms of declarative sentences; his own life being invested in syntax. He must of necessity assume that Hemingway's style was a matter of being an athletic youth sufficiently clever to pick up some tricks from Gertrude Stein to serve his ambition.

Hemingway's emulators thought so too. For his art was so hidden it seemed easily imitated: one had only to talk tough and cut it short. Some imitated him boldly, some secretly, some mockingly and some slavishly.* But what they wrote had no tension: his prose was invulnerable.

Though his prose was invulnerable, his life was not. He flaunted a personality as poetic as Byron's and as challenging as Teddy Roosevelt's; before timorous men whose lives were prosaic. It was necessary, no, absolutely *essential,* to get his number.

"He thinks like a child," someone remembered Goethe saying of Byron. So Norman Mailer said "Hemingway has never written anything that would disturb an eight-year-old." So

---

* See *Something of Value* by Robert Ruark, a novel slack as a severed clothesline.

Professor Fiedler said it and Professor Podhoretz said it and Professor Edel said it and Professor Macdonald said it. First they said it one by one. Then, gathering courage, they all said it together in chorus: Now we have his number: Now we *really* have his number.

And of all our thinkers, from Paul Goodman to Ronald Reagan, who has given us a passage so certain not to disturb an eight-year-old as this:

"If you serve time for society, democracy, and the other things quite young, and declining any further enlistment make yourself responsible only to yourself, you exchange the pleasant, comfortable stench of comrades for something you can never feel in any other way than by yourself. That something I cannot define completely but the feeling comes ... when, on the sea, you are alone with it and know that this Gulf Stream you are living with, knowing, learning about, and loving, has moved, as it moves, since before man, and that it has gone by the shoreline of that long, beautiful, unhappy island since before Columbus sighted it and that the things you find out about it, and those that have always lived in it are permanent and of value because that stream will flow, as it had flowed, after the Indians, after the Spaniards, after the British, after the Americans and after all the Cubans and all the systems of government, the richness, the poverty, martyrdom, the sacrifice and the venality and the cruelty are all gone as the high-piled scow of garbage, bright-colored, white-flecked, ill-smelling, now tilted on its side, spills off its load into the blue water, turning it a pale green to a depth of four or five fathoms as the load spreads across the surface, the sinkable part going down and the flotsam of palm-fronds, corks, bottles, and used electric light-globes, seasoned with an occasional condom or a deep floating corset, the torn leaves of a student's exercise book, a well-inflated dog, the occasional rat, the no-longer-distinguished cat; all this well shepherded by the boats of the garbage pickers who pluck their prizes with long poles, as interested, as intelligent, and as accurate as historians; they have the viewpoint; the stream, with no visible flow, takes five loads of this a day when things are going well in La Habana and in ten miles along the coast it is as clear and blue and unimpressed as it was ever before the tug hauled out the scow; and the palm-fronds of our victories, the worn light-bulbs of our discoveries and the empty condoms of our great loves float with no significance against one single lasting thing—the stream."

Call that babytalk.

July 14th: Rafts of a Summer Night

Every morning of that lost summer came as a fresh surprise: a sallow youth wearing a bright red sweater practiced walking a tightwire right next door! He traversed the air from his back porch to his little garage, glided to the ground, then trotted lightly. We cheered as though the circus had come to our neighborhood. Nothing like it had ever happened on our street before.

He never spoke. My father called him "The Greenhorn"—but from what green country he had come he never told.

Yet we knew that the green country to which he went was Wisconsin. In the first hours after Friday night had fallen, when every back porch wavered, like rafts of a summer night, with the pinpointed flares of sticks of punk; that we burned, and moved as we burned them, to ward off mosquitoes, Greenhorn cranked up his Model-T and wheeled off to some county fair. I went to the backyard gate to watch him go: his taillight winked *Goodbye Forever* to me.

Goodbye to summer, goodbye to fun: goodbye to the weekday-morning sun.

Until a triumphant Monday-forenoon honking and a neighbor's cry—"Greener back! On wire going up!" brought summer back in a Model-T.

He rode the air and we rode the fence and the very air seemed daring.

Strangely, I anticipated scenes yet greater to come.

They came.

Greener soldered a pulley onto an ironworker's helmet, turned himself upside-down in it and rolled, upsy-downsy, along a cable to his garage!

A burst of applause—then he hit the ground on his face. Bashing his forehead and bending the hell out of the pulley.

"Greener's balance is so good upside-down he can't walk to the garage straight up anymore," my mother commented— and rapped me one that spun me half across the kitchen—"let that be a warning to *you!*" A warning not to walk straight up to a garage or not to glide upside-down to it I didn't know.

Yet in that week nobody walked the wonderful wire. Greener had holed up in his garage. He was sleeping in there now.

"He hasn't come out for two days," my mother reported to my father.

"He's *thinking*," I assured them.

What Greener thought of was a double-cable, one length tightened from porch to garage and a lower strand drawn from garage to porch.

I saw the problem: how would he make it to the lower strand? When, through his garage window, I saw him somersaulting on an old mattress, I got the idea.

He came out of the garage somersaulting. Cheers—then apprehensive silence as he clamped on the helmet, slid on the cable straight-up to the garage; balanced himself upside-down on the wire—then somersaulted onto the lower strand and glided triumphantly home!

I stood on my head in upside-down joy. My father whacked the upside until I put it down—"Why can't you be a good boy like I was when I was a boy?" he wanted to know. I didn't know why, but no whacking could lessen my joy: a man had but to be foolishly daring and the world was changed, from sunlessness to sun, for everyone.

Hard times returned to the back porches of home. Greener had to travel farther, and take greater risks with his neck, for less money. One Monday the Model-T ran out of gas five blocks from home and we had to push it—half a dozen other kids and myself—to his garage. He did not wheel away to a county fair the next Friday evening: no gas.

"Greener will think of something," I promised my mother.

"May it be to walk on his feet," she hoped.

Greener thought of something. He jacked up the Model-T and crawled underneath it. He was converting it to a kerosene-oil burner. My father took alarm.

"The Stanley Steamer has already been invented!" he called the news down to Greener through the car's open hood—"It doesn't work out!"

Greener crawled out, looked up at my father, shook his head—yes—for *him* it would work out. And crawled back under the hood. His will was forged of the same stuff as his tightwire cable. But it wasn't as flexible.

Now he lay against the November earth. In the slant yellow light of the last of day, coldly framing his garage door, we glimpsed the soles of his ragged sneakers, and saw his toes twitching with the cold. After dark he worked on by candle-light. It looked like the good times were over.

"If that boy had a mind he'd be dangerous," my father felt.

"He's only saving electricity," my mother hoped.

"He'll wind up in a room without corners," my father decided.

"May he never lift anything heavier than money," my mother wished.

Her washing was whipping whitely in the bright blue win-ter weather when a long, low, dripageous pall of coal-oil smog, sufficiently light to clear fences but too soggy to clear a clothes-line, emerged from the hood of the Model-T, enwrapping sheets, shirts, petticoats, panties and pants, blankets and hand-kerchiefs, pillowcases and flannel underwear, leaving line after line dragging blackly toward earth.

Some Stanley Steamer.

Through this belching pall two policemen groped, with flashlight and gun, ready for anything. When Greener did not respond to a billy rapping the soles of his sneakers, one cop seized one naked ankle and the other seized the other, and dragged him forth, looking more like a miner coming up from a cave-in than an acrobat. Under the coal-oil his face was ashen. On the step of the hurry-up wagon he stumbled. I laughed.

It was like seeing a cat trip over itself.

Ten days later he returned, with a shuffling, brokenhearted walk. The Room Without Corners had done for that pale youth.

For neither upright nor upside-down, Greener never walked another wire. Nor wheeled off to farewells waved by small pinpointed flares from back porches on either side of his steering wheel. Nor ever in honking triumph returned.

Greener went to work in a neighborhood factory that man-ufactured endless belting for other factories. The acrobat stood at an endless belt making belting endlessly. He grew thin.

First he worked on wide-belt belting, but, as he grew still thinner, he was transferred to narrow-belt belting. There he began to gain weight. Greener had begun drinking.

He began drinking as soon as he had finished making belt-ing endlessly, and his drinking went on all night without end. When he began drinking as endlessly as he tended to belting, he was replaced by a beltless machine that makes machines for manufacturing endless belting.

Greener never tried anything again. His summer had been brief, the applause only fleeting, the good times soon done. The first heavy frost split the kitchen pane of the house in which he had once lived. One of the cables, that he'd drawn so tightly, snapped under its burden of ice; entangling itself with the lower cable. At last both wires hung uselessly dangling. I felt disappointed in everything. In March I shattered the window of his garage.

From time to time, in winters that followed, I saw Greener, diminished to a beer-drinking fly of the tavern corners, again. On the kind of night when cats freeze on fire escapes, I watched him shuffling about a bar with a shot-glass of whiskey on his head, inviting somebody to knock it off and make the whiskey run into his eyes, because some of it ran into his mouth. Once a bartender put him down on all fours and rode him across the floor, standing up in the saddle and then bringing his full weight down on his horse. Greener sprawled, rolled over laughing, onto his back, and lay with his mouth wide until the bartender paid for his ride with a shot of bar whiskey; that he sloshed down Greener's throat.

There was simply no end of the fun when Greener was in good form. People don't know what good times *are* any more.

*

Wandering about a Mammoth Cave of the paperback trade, through a fluorescent basement mist a few days before I boarded this ship, was what had brought the memory of Greener back. For it returned a phrase I'd read long ago— "We don't even know what living is now"—as though, watching men and women adrift through an underground glow, it

101

wasn't titles of books we were seeking, but the names of our true selves.

Even the titles seemed adrift: *The Quest of Meaning, The Quest of Man, Man's Quest, The Quest of Being, The Meaning of Man, Meaning and Existence*—they began revolving as on some endless unseen belt. I closed my eyes and held on.

When I opened them the titles had steadied, yet they were still there: *Man's Destiny, Man's Hope, Man's Fate, Man's Place, The Past of Man, The Path of Man, Hillbilly Nympho* —now how had *that* gotten in Man's path?—*Be Glad You're Single, Be Glad You're Neurotic, Be Glad You're Ugly, Be Glad You're Paraplegic, Be Glad You're White*—isn't anybody *pleased* to be black anymore? *Be Glad You're You, Be Glad You're Absurd, Growing Up Absurd*—is Paul Goodman arranging our booklists? What is more absurd than to be so grown-up that the Meaning of Man concerns you more than men and women? Since when does abstracting the life from the poetry of living entitle a hollow hack to the honorable name of thinker?

I saw three biographies of Melville but not a copy of *Typee;* four studies of Dostoevsky but where was *Crime and Punishment?* About D. H. Lawrence the safest statement anyone can now make is that yet another "definitive edition" of his work will be issued within the year, although eleven of his books are out of print—definitively. Who hooked *that* tightwire up? Would their publication dump all "definitive editions" onto the remainder tables? Who's standing on his head now?

"Where are they? Where are they?" were Dylan Thomas' last coherent words.

They went thataway.

Our most daring minds, from Mailer to Murph the Surf,

are now so high above ground with no net below, that the only people still looking up are those on pot.

"What I really object to," one Home Ec thinker claims, "is the writer who offers me the world's horrors without offering a solution"; * thus advising us that Flaubert behaved badly in sending *Madame Bovary* to the publisher without appending a solution to small-town adultery. (That the world offers hardly a horror more deadly than a bourgeois antiquarian imposing a merchandiser's morality upon all art not subserving his personal comfort, he is too complacent to suspect.)

Dostoevsky's underground man, born from an idea instead of a father, lost and confused when left alone without books —a creature who did not know what living was—has strangely risen bearing a critic's credentials.

And the word to the Pfc instructor, wherever faculty brass and their wives compete for captaincies, is *publish, publish, publish*. Riding an endless belt of useless information, he becomes confident that the footnote is the road to fame and fortune. The present imbalance of books *about* writing, to those written from direct experience, is sufficient evidence of this. And sends throngs of young people to believing that literature derives from other books rather than from life.

They are duped by a presumption: that the truths which can sustain them can be handed down by educators, critics, analysts, anthologists and professional distributors of safe precepts: all those who, like Greener losing his sense of life under the hood of a secondhand Ford, lose theirs in a world where terminology embalms alike the living with the dead. The man whose passion attained its peak in a course in cost accounting now emerges as a shaper of American letters.

How else to explain that a compilation of literary allusions

* Edmund Fuller in *Saturday Review*.

such as *Herzog,* possessing no value beyond cuteness, can be mistaken for a living book? The explanation is that dedication to accuracy no more suffices to make criticism true than does correctness in a novelist: lacking a sense of poetry, all creative work becomes false.

"What I have termed 'evasion' in his work," another big-spender-around-campus explains Hemingway, "will be borne out if we search for its roots in his life, from which an artist's work always springs. To be able to cope with emotion only by indirection [is] like escaping from life by big-game hunting or watching violence in the bullring. These are fascinating pursuits for our hours of leisure when given proper perspective. When they become a substitute for other forms of life they become an evasion of life." *

This is spite-burning; not criticism. When my father scolded me—"Why can't you be a good boy?"—he was being quite as critical while being more just. And his English was better. But then he wasn't a terminologist whose morality depended upon personal security.

That "always and everywhere the proper study of mankind is man" doesn't mean to annotate Man but to live like one. The critic's resentment here is that which the small shop-keeper has always felt for the restless wanderer. What business does anyone have, he is asking, following bullfighters from arena to arena when he could be having a rich, full life teaching young women iambic pentameter? Why go bumping in a jeep across a battlefield when one can go wheeling contentedly to class in a Porsche?

There, *there,* between the "definitive edition" and the bursar's office, between the hard cover and the soft, between an

* "The Art of Evasion" by Leon Edel, in *Hemingway. A Collection of Critical Essays* edited by Robert P. Weeks.

LL.D. and his next *critique,* is where annotated man faces up
to a life of no evasions.

Hemingway's life could be told solely in terms of his hos-
tility toward the *petit bourgeois* demand that neither love nor
death be real. That he overstates his proofs does not now
lessen the usefulness of his voyage. He began with *Nada,* he
ended with *Nada:* but he knew those ports-of-call where life
conflicts with death. He made the voyage.

For the risks he took were not unmeasured. Both physical
and literary, they were the calculated chances of a pro. His
risks were of the kind that, failing, the taker fails alone; but
succeeding, succeed for everyone. To be qualified to pass
judgment upon his style, therefore, a critic would himself
have to be a man willing to take similar risks. Since no such
man appeared during Hemingway's career, his work remains
to be judged.

Villon, writing in the fifteenth century, brings Hemingway
to us more justly than any modern critic:

> *In my own country I am in a far-off land*
> *I am strong but have no force nor power*
> *I win all yet remain a loser*
> *At break of day I say goodnight*
> *When I lie down I have great fear of falling*

More than any other contemporary, Hemingway put the
ancestral warning, that he who gains his life shall lose it, into
terms usable by modern man. Of many American writers who
represented their own times, Hemingway alone made his
times represent him.

For the painter no longer in touch with people who don't
look at pictures begins to die as a painter. The actor whose
life has moved from the marketplace to the studio acts falsely.
The novelist, grown remote from people who don't read, be-

comes untrue to those who do read. The thinker who loses contact with those who never think at all, no longer thinks justly.

As the critic whose only wellspring is the work of other men at last gets to know all there is to know about Literature.

Except how to enjoy it.

July 15th: Arabian Sea

Between the ceaseless rocking of the sea and the ceaseless wordiness of the critics, I divided the hours until afternoon. Then I decided to visit the officer's lounge for a cup of coffee and witty conversation.

A ward for catatonics would have been as lively and the coffee might have been better. First Mate, Third Mate, First Engineer and Second, each sat by himself looking straight ahead with his assigned cup before him. Each had his rating, so no more words were needed. What was there to do the rest of one's days but avoid gonorrhea?

William Gibbs McAdoo Manning, Chief Purser, was the philosopher of this likable group. When I came in he had just finished not replying to something the First Mate hadn't said. The Second Engineer appeared to be in agreement.

I noticed that the sugar-shaker was empty but, rather than ask for sugar, I drank the coffee black: why stick *my* neck out?

The thinking seemed to be to take death's mouth softly to one's own, in order to escape the risk of living. This, in the flesh, was the American affliction of living incommunicado even to oneself.

One deck down the seaborne sadsacks, foulups and misfits from every state in the union were lounging around reading comic books. Chips was listening on a transistor to the Dodgers playing the Giants.

Smith motioned to me.

"You remind me of a fellow I knew once"—Smith adjusted his neck and shifted a hip (to favor his Monstrous Boil) in order to get me into his sightline—"because his face was purely honest, but all he was good at was stealing."

"Thanks," I acknowledged Smith's flattering way.

"His name was Zekl," Smith went blithely on, "and the way he was most different from you was that *he* was *fat*. Zekl was *all* fat. He carried an outfielder's mitt on his hip from the time he'd played semi-pro ball but now he could barely waddle. We called him 'Hippo'—now ain't *that* a diller?"

I didn't see any diller.

"Hippo Zekl was a good center-fielder on Sundays and a good Saturday-Night-Mover. A Saturday-Night-Mover is a fellow who helps cops move stuff out of back-doors Saturday nights. This was in the days before night baseball so his athletic career didn't interfere with his criminal life."

Smith hitched his neck: it was going to be a long story.

"One Saturday night he helped move 10,500 dollars' worth of office furniture out of an office-furniture place, and the next day I was playing center and Hippo was in right. It was the last of the ninth, we were one run behind, there was two out 'n nobody on. Zekl came to bat.

"He sliced the first pitch toward first 'n should of been out by five feet, except the first-baseman waited for the pitcher to field it and the pitcher waited for the first-baseman, then both made the move together just as Zekl slood—"

"He *what?*"

"Slood. Slood into first. He was trying to beat the baseman to the bag with the ball. So he slood."

Smith looked perfectly guileless.

"Go on," I encouraged him.

"He brought up such a cloud of dust that nobody could

tell what had happened till the dust cleared. Then we seen Zekl standing on the bag and the first baseman looking for the ball.

"He made sure the baseman wasn't trying the hidden ball play on him. Then he took off for second. This time he slood spikes-first."

Smith glanced at me to see whether I had any objection. I had none.

"When Zekl made second, he seen that the pitcher was helping the first-baseman find the ball, so he said to the second-baseman, 'I guess you fellows just don't want me'—and took off for third. This time he slood right *under* the baseman. When he got up and begin dusting hisself off, the right-fielder came in to help find the ball before Zekl took off again, because now there was nobody left but the catcher to stop him. But Zekl just stood on the bag as if we didn't have four dollars apiece going on him.

" 'Home!' we hollered at him. 'Home, Hippo! Home!'

"Zekl began *strolling* toward home like he had all day.

" '*Slide*, Zekl! *Slide!*' everybody began hollering."

"And he *slood?*"

"No *sir*," Smith told me reproachfully, "he *didn't* slide. He took the ball out of his own pocket and tossed it to the catcher when he was still ten feet from the plate. The catcher got so excited he put Zekl out by shoving the ball in his face. Zekl sat down in the middle of the base-path saying the same thing over and over."

"What was he saying over and over?"

" 'I had it coming,' Zekl kept saying, 'I had it coming.' "

Smith looked at me smugly confident I would be unsatisfied with the story.

"What was the final score?" I wanted to know.

"Five-four. We lost."

I turned away, but felt his hand on my shoulder lightly. I turned back.

"That wasn't what you were supposed to ask, sir."

"What was I supposed to ask?"

"You were supposed to ask why this fellow got hisself thrown out and then just sat there saying he had it coming."

"Why did he get hisself thrown out and just sat there saying the same thing over and over?"

"Well, he said, 'I had it coming, I had it coming,' because his conscience bothered him about trying to steal a baseball. *That's* what he *claimed* later."

"And what about the ten thousand dollars' worth of office equipment he'd moved the night before?" I asked.

" '*Everybody* moves office equipment on Saturday nights,' was the way Zekl felt about *that*—'but no *good* guy,' he told me, 'no really *good* guy *ever* slides into first. Nobody *ever* slides into first,' he went around saying. That's what he'd meant when he kept saying 'I got it coming, I got it coming.' It wasn't office equipment on his conscience. He'd got hisself thrown out at home because he didn't think a fellow who slood into first *deserved* to score a run."

"Frankie Frisch did," I reminded Smith.

Smith jerked his neck a notch inward.

"You're putting me on."

"I'm not putting you on," I told him irritably, "he *slood* fingers-first, on his chest, into first, at the Polo Grounds. It started a riot."

Smith studied me.

"If it started a riot," he decided thoughtfully, "then he must have."

He put out his hand and I took it.

"Thanks for telling me that. I feel better now."

"Because *you* were the guy who slood into first?"

110

He grinned.

"You G-Twoed it, sir," he told me with fresh respect—"you hit it right on the head. Never was *nobody* called Hippo Zekl. I made up the name because I was ashamed of what I done. You've took a weight off my conscience. Thank you. I appreciate it. Any time I can do anything for you, sir, you have only to let me know."

"You could fill me in on why the last stitch goes through the nose any time you feel in the mood," I suggested.

Smith nodded as though he'd anticipated my question.

"Let me make a *suggestion,* sir," he told me without seeming offended, "ask Chips. It's *his* job, not mine."

We were three days from the port of Bombay.

Port of Bombay

I. Into the Gala Day

THIS street, when the land was British, was named *Saféd-Galli:* Avenue of the White Whores. Today it is the Street of the Hundred Cages. Not everybody went home.

Those who stayed do a lot of spitting. The walks in front of their cages are streaked by ropes of spittle of blackish red. A platinum blond with purple lips puts out her tongue; and her tongue is a deadlier purple yet. She smiles and the smile fills with blood: these ominous splatters marking the public ways are betel. The girls of the public cages chew it to dull hunger.

Some go into the cages for shelter. Some are waifs who were snatched off the streets to earn their keep as servants until they grew big enough to be used. Some are working off fines for husbands and brothers. Betel is easier to spit out than debt.

India's bureaucracies are accused of using too much paper; around the cages of Suklaji Street it uses none at all. Any tourist can become an official jail visitor just by pausing long enough to say, "Hello, Baby." By dispensing with paper-work entailed in making out visitors' passes, an enormous saving is being effected for the nation. What India will do with the money is India's problem.

The areaways, where boys wearing saris wait, seem less streaked by betel. *"No mama, no papa—you give,"* one cries in light mockery after me. His sari looks wound in mockery of himself; and of all Bombay's grinning amputees, contented bearers of incurable afflictions, flaunters of unnamed and un-namable diseases; and rouged gimps who plead languidly.

Yet the woman extending her palm upturned to me through bars of wood, while giving suck to her infant, isn't mocking me. Her breasts are wrinkled.

Nor that lank youth naked to his loincloth, balancing a bicycle against himself and shading his eyes with his hand while standing in cowdung. He ducks into a doorway, emerges with a red umbrella hooked to his cloth, mounts the bicycle and wheels merrily away. When you work for West-ern Union it doesn't matter *what* your're standing in.

The girl's voice bouncing in from an American army base, through shop, taxi and bazaar, is that of Pat Suzuki—

Daddy, I want a diamond ring—

"The proper season for rain is the present, sir," a voice in low-rolling thunder warns me—"yet the entire month, we are empty!"

Two eyes, threaded by yellowish filament and filmed by cunning, looked up at me from under my armpit like two olives in a bowl of buttermilk. The man was almost as wide as he was high, and as dark as he was sweaty; with the head of a lion so long caged its mane has fallen to ruin.

"O, Bombay is a great city, my friend—nobody knows how many people there are in Bombay, sir—multitudes!"—here The Lion daubed at his forehead with a handkerchief, taking care to flutter it against my lapel so I could see it was silk—"a great city and one with much traffic! Yet not a drop of rain! Nature finds herself scourged: friendship falls off: brothers divide. In cities, mutinies. In countries, discord. In palaces, treason. Bonds cracked between son and father"—I sensed his

116

touch go down my belt then lightly withdraw. I'd never been
frisked before by anyone who could quote *Lear* while doing
it. It was my first time.

Anyhow the transistor was on my other side.

"A hundred and fifty inches of rain once fell in five days at
Cherripunji! Yet *here*"—he turned his palms so wide yet so
empty up to a blind sun—"Empty, sir, a city of empty multitudes! *'We must do something i' the heat!'* "—and closed his
pitch with a smile so snaky it wriggled out of his perspiration.

The girl giving suck to her infant still had her palm upturned at me through the bars. The platinum blonde again
put out her tongue. The lank youth on the bike was lost in
the traffic's endless pleading. The dreadful day of big Bombay
burned on.

While Pat sang on and on—

Daddy, you got to get the best for me . . .

Yet Daddy never replied.

"Sir!" The Lion introduced himself with a command that
sounded like "Atten-*shun!*"—"Sir! *I* am Baliram! Thirty-five
years in Customs!"—then coyly waggling a warning finger
playfully at me—"Beware, my American friend! I may come
aboard *your* ship! Baliram may inspect *your* quarters! O, you
won't know Baliram in uniform! Baliram knows the tricks!
Watch out, my friend, or your visit may cost you a pretty
penny!"—then that smile like a pang gone yellow with servility.

Suddenly shifting to a man-to-man approach, The Lion
became all manliness and candor—"Baliram is no angel to be
sure. Baliram knows the places seamen go. It has not been so
long that Baliram has forgotten his own sins. Baliram too was
young"—I had to keep turning slightly from him as he moved,
to keep him off the transistor—"*A man may see how this*

117

world goes with no eyes" he assured me—"but have you ever spent an evening in an Anglo-Indian parlor, my friend? Have you seen the little ones playing contentedly on the kitchen floor while the Anglo-Indian mother cooks and the father reads Dickens aloud?" I wondered who was listening to father reading in the parlor while everyone else was busy on the kitchen floor. "Have you seen a home God watches over, my friend?"

"No," I had to admit, "but I once knew a girl who roomed with the Alton Giant."

The Lion pretended to laugh. "You *are* pulling my leg, my friend— How can there be trust between men unless they begin with respect?" His fingers brushed a corner of the transistor.

"Sir, my car is at the corner. Let me *show* you an Anglo-Indian home." He linked my arm in his. This old boy really wanted me.

He waved a taxi to the curb, climbed in beside the driver and began giving directions in the tone one would use to one's chauffeur, with a condescending hand on the driver's shoulder.

"O, my friend, you don't know our people," he resumed, "you hear nothing but cries of *baksheesh! baksheesh!* so you think we think of nothing but *baksheesh*. My friend, let me tell you. We do not *all* live as you see the ones of Suklaji Street live. We are the most spiritual of peoples. In our humble Anglo-Indian homes you will see The Golden Rule come true!"

I looked out the window to see if there were a good movie in town. Under a sky stained by betel we wheeled midst the blind, overtaking the maimed, and abandoning the dying. Come to The Land of the Golden Rule! Opportunity knocks in bustling Bombay! Here at last, I perceived, was a city

118

where I might not only get a start in life—but a *headstart!* For I outweighed almost everybody and even the ones my own size were non-violent. Nothing stood in my way.

"Madam"—I began practicing a pitch of my own—"Do you find cataracts troublesome? This little bottle of Magic Chalmugra Oil cures cataracts, leukemia, leprosy, the falling sickness, hernia and gangrene—only seventy-five rupees per bottle. Thank you, madam. You need a small loan in order to marry, sir? Happy to help you—leave your wife at the fourth cage from the left, Falkland Road and Suklaji Street. You say you are well known as The Cha-Cha Queen, young woman? How would you like to give private dancing lessons to American seamen on long- or short-term rates?"

Come to The Land of Non-Violence! The One Democracy where everyone has the same opportunity of leaping into a taxi beside its passenger and saying *"Ssssssss—you like nice gel, sor?"* If he looks like he'd prefer riding alone, get hold of a finger and *smile. Breathe* on him. If he still doesn't break try *"Ssssssss—you like nice boy, sor?"* Then claw him lightly, blow in his ear and *get out.* Americans solve spiritual issues violently and *we* are a non-violent people.

Never forget—*no violence, no violence, no violence.*

There's big money to be made in India mugging the mutilated. Earn while you learn! A pretty penny can be picked up robbing the lame when they're sleeping. Something for everybody in bustling Bombay! Learn to fall headlong in front of a gharry! Dad! Be a leper and own your own bell! Sis! Be a girl *dēvi-dāsi* and give suck to your young behind bars! Junior! Learn to make friends with seamen and wear jade earrings! Granny! Be an old abandoned *ayah* and scratch strangers from a prone position! Get your left arm sliced off at the elbow and pick up alms with your right! Did somebody leave the knees out of your legs? Stick your foot in your

119

mouth and learn to roll! Make a pile overnight stuffing hash-ish into condoms! Come to The One Democracy that squats to pee! *But: no violence   no violence   no violence.*

I couldn't be sure that I wasn't still in Chicago.

Miracle of Todd-A-O, I saw, was showing at the Strand. Jerry Lewis was due at the Regal. *Kwality Ice-Creams with Soft-Recorded Music* flashed past between chop suey joints and hamburger stands. Where the hell *was* The Mysterious East?

"The offense of throwing articles at members of the judiciary," Baliram saw fit I should know, "is increasing in Bombay, sir. Only last week Mr. Sarjero hurled a shoe at President Magistrate Chinoy in the Mazagon Court. Fortunately it struck an advocate. Persons of this type menace our society, sir. I am of those who feel that, unless deterrent sentences are imposed, it will not be long before disorder will reign in our courts."

"What happened to the nut who threw the shoe?" I asked.

"Two years' rigorous imprisonment. He was fortunate. He might well have received five."

A kid with his left arm sliced off raggedly at the elbow climbed into the seat beside me and shoved the elbow into my face. It was festering nicely.

"Papa! You give!"

I gave him a dime to take it away. He handed the dime back: not enough.

"Now you don't get anything," I decided firmly.

After all, *I* hadn't sliced it off.

The kid began working up a spittle and in no time at all had a great froth going. I handed him a quarter and he leaped out laughing. The old man smiled. He knew, I knew, everybody knew I *had* sliced it off.

What India specializes in is chicken curry and redemptive

120

beggary: the Indian takes such contentment in affliction he wants to share it. All that yummy agony, all that festering horror is yours as well as his. When he lays it on you, it *stays* there. Then leaps out laughing.

Yet: no violence. No violence. No violence.

Anthony Quinn in Carl Foreman's GUNS OF NAVARONE flashed past. Hi, Tony. Hi, Carl. How's Greg?

"Do you see that innocent-looking hack-Victoria?" Baliram cut in. "Do you notice the bales of hay beneath for the horses? Only last Tuesday the Yellow Gate police found a radio transistor at the Red Gate, concealed in just such innocent bales!"

"What the hell are the *Yellow Gate* police doing at the *Red Gate?*" I asked him—"Why don't they stay in their own precinct?"

A face framed by shoulder-length hair and fever obtruded itself into the cab window, but at my shout of dismay—"No! No!" it withdrew looking shocked. *That's* how to deal with interviewers from *Time.*

I poked my head out to see if anyone from *Playboy* was around but couldn't see a soul wearing a pith helmet.

"And only yesterday the police stopped a gharry on Falkland Road—at the very point where we met today—and discovered not one transistor in the hay—but another in the tool-box!"

You're cutting in closer all the time, Dad, I reflected. I may have to jump ship and pan elsewhere for gold. But so long as I was seeing the city I might as well keep riding away from the madding throng, I decided.

Even though my guide seemed more of a fink every minute.

The throng got more and more madding. The nearer to his little Anglo-Indian nest Baliram got, the finkier he sounded and the worse the American movies got.

The cab stopped for a light and I crouched, but a *rap-rap-*

rap on the door straightened me up—a boy selling balloons, with his left leg tied back to a pole. It was the pole he was using to rap the taxi-door, leaning on the car to do so. I grabbed a balloon, handed him a dime and the Sikh started the car and the kid fell in the road before I could get my change.

He sprawled on his face holding fast to his balloons. This was also my fault.

"Don't start up so fast," I scolded the Sikh—"I had a nickel coming."

And away we wheeled without a woe into the gala day.

Five Branded Women was at the Rex. Would they show the actual branding? That was one show I didn't plan to miss.

"A curious incident of only last Sunday," the old man's low rumble resumed, "a spider was discovered in an aerated bottle! Now the Health Officer has asked the people to consume aerated water only after the most careful examination!"

I liked my balloon. It wasn't young any more but I liked it all the more for that. It was fever-red stippled with small yellow disease spots but they weren't malign. I could tell because they weren't festering. Not yet.

A cat raced across the street grinning with glee at the possibility of being squashed under wheels. He made the curb by a whisker and then stood on the curb looking disappointed: he was going to make another try.

"Nonetheless, the situation is good for The Free World," The Lion assured me, "your General Taylor saw that in South Viet Nam last week and had the courage to say so."

A girl put her head in the window and howled, *"Bly-eye-nd brother! Blye-eye-nd brother!"*

She wasn't lying. When I put my head out the window I saw him. He wasn't just *blind:* he was the Blindest. He didn't even have to roll his eyes to show *he* was blinder than anybody. Somebody had left his irises out.

"Get him contact lenses," I advised, and gave her a nickel. I would have made it a dime but I didn't want to corrupt her.

Geraldine Page was at the Alexander in *Summer and Smoke*.

I became absorbed in watching a man so thin his bones cast shadows: six feet high, with a growth of beard and hair, holding a bit of burlap across his genitals. Except for that burlap he was bare—ass naked in the middle of town. What a market for burlap!

"Sir," the old man insisted, "only today my friend Ayub Sardar Mulani was arrested by the General Crime Branch for breach of trust—what a dishonor to come upon gray hairs! Over a thousand pounds embezzled since the first of the year! —and admits everything freely! 'Now that God is dead, my Mistress is my Heaven,' he told the arresting officer, but his mistress threatened to leave him if he didn't move her to a more respectable heaven. She may be an angel to Sardar, she told him, but people were looking at her as though she were a whore. So he stole to save his angel's honor. We are a people who prize honor over everything, sir."

"So long as he didn't spend anything on himself they can't touch him," I assured my old man as the cab wheeled up before a yellow cabaret.

Baliram projected his great bulk backwards out of the hack and waddled, frontwards, to a door beside the cabaret; leaving me to settle with his "chauffeur." I followed his monstrous bottom up a flight of careworn stairs into a room crowded with fixtures of another day. There was faint music, as of someone playing a piano only for himself, from the cabaret below. Overhead a wooden ceiling fan beat monotonously.

123

My balloon tossed in its breeze—I'd have to be careful not to get it caught in *that*.

"I want you to meet my wife," Baliram assured me— "*Pawm!*" he bawled, "*Pawmela! We hawv a gist, Pawmela!*"

All the pictures around the room were of the Stations of the Cross; and of such size that the room itself was diminished. The old man had a bigger stake in the legends of Christianity than in its real estate, it looked like. I wondered whether anybody was being crucified in the kitchen.

"*Pawm,*" he called out in a tone most affected, "*Pawmela dee*-ah! We have a *gist,* Pawmela deeah!"

The girl who emerged from the kitchen was another Caucasianized slant; one, I guessed, from the hills of Burma or the plains of Assam, with eyebrows penciled high to make her eyes look round. Her name would, more appropriately, have been Kai-Li. She didn't crack a smile at sight of an American holding a red balloon. This was to show me she was British to the bone.

"Do you like our little home, sir?" Baliram asked me.

No farther than I can throw my old balloon, I thought.

The girl nodded coldly once; then slipper-sloppered back to her kitchen-station.

"*Pawm* deah. *Pawm*ela. I would like you to *welcome* ouah gist."

So here comes Pawm slipper-sloppering back. If she'd put in as much care on her dress as on her eyebrows, two buttons wouldn't have been askew. Pawm wasn't more than twenty-two but she walked like sixty-six. Pawm just didn't *care*.

"How do," she acknowledged both me and my balloon, and started away again.

"*Pawm*ela, our guest would like a bit of Anglo-Indian cheeah with us— *Would* you mind stepping out for it?"

124

"Where's the bread?" Her English was faultless.

"O, I'm suah ouah guest will be glad to contribute a few rupees toward some Anglo-Indian cheeah," the old man decided airily.

I extended a five-dollar bill toward him, and when he reached for it I gave him my index finger instead.

Immediately he feigned great amusement. "*Pawm*ela! Did you see the *trick?* O, *will* you teach me how *that* is done, sir? See, deah—he offers money but then gives nothing but a finger! It is done to reprove persons who act greedily— O, but wasn't it neatly accomplished!"

The girl blushed. He was too much for me too.

I gave her enough change to buy a bottle and she shuffled out into the hallway.

"I'm interested in radio engineering," Baliram informed me, indicating a radio disassembled on a mantel—"on occasion I buy old sets in hope of repairing them for resale. Unfortunately," he shrugged—"I have little skill along mechanical lines. Perhaps you would care to trust me with your balloon long enough to take off your coat? You'd feel more at ease."

Sitting down at the table and letting the balloon catch the breeze from the fan, yet not letting it get too near the blades, I indicated I was at ease already.

Pawmela returned with a bottle. Baby, I thought, that was a fast trip to the still, considering you didn't even use the stairs. Either you went down the side of the building or the Liquor Permit Office is in the hall.

"*Pawm!* May we have *glaw*sses?"

Pawm slid a couple glasses across the table and turned back to the kitchen before they stopped sliding. I knew they'd like me in Bombay.

Baliram filled my glass, then his own. I waited to see whether he'd drink it or quote *Lear* to gain time. I gave him

125

time and he downed the drink, so I followed: a rich blend
of Jamaican rum and rotting bananas.

"We would *both* feel more at home if you took off your
coat, my friend," he urged me.

The balloon was a problem. When I tried taking off my
coat I found it wouldn't go through my sleeve. Finally the
old man held it for me until I got my coat off. When he
handed it back I pulled the transistor out of my belt, extended
its aerial and tuned it in—all with one hand.

It isn't fair for you to want me

a tenor's voice came in pleadingly—

You only want me for today—

"That's Tokyo," I assured Baliram so he wouldn't think
it was Atlanta.

"What price are you asking, my friend?" he asked me.

"Sixty dollars American."

"I'm only a poor broker," he explained. "I can't buy it
myself."

"I don't care who I sell to."

He examined the brand name, fussed with the aerial, tuned
in another station, expressed doubt, shook his head regretfully. He wanted to tune it in again; so I drew the aerial
down.

"I *can* get sixty dollars for it," he decided, "but no more.
That leaves me nothing for the risk I take in your interest."

"Everything you get over fifty-five is yours," I compromised.
"If you don't get over fifty-five you take the risk for nothing."
Some compromise.

"And if I get less?"

"Then you deduct the difference between what you got
and fifty-five and that much is what you're out."

126

"You drive a hard bargain, my friend."

"I can get seventy-five for it myself," I lied.

He stood up wiping his forehead in anticipation of the heat of the street, went into the kitchen, and returned with a shopping bag and two loaves of French bread. He put the set in the bottom of the bag with the loaves sticking out; and left walking more heavily than before.

I was left alone with a pint of cheap rum and Kai-Li.

The girl waited till the old man's heavy step had died away before she came out. She'd tidied her hair, touched her lips and eyebrows; but still looked sullen. I invited her to share the rum.

"Me no drink," she explained; but sat down all the same.

I waited.

"Papa no good," she told me at last, "Mama no good. Everybody no good."

Then merely sat looking at me as though suspecting I was probably worse. There wasn't a thing she could do for me and there wasn't a thing I could do for her. Except to listen to her woes.

That she plainly wanted to tell. For they were the kind one can safely tell only to a stranger.

I tied the balloon to my finger.

"You like the old man?" I encouraged her.

She wrinkled her nose. "I do like he tell," she told me, "I got no paper."

"No passport?"

"No nothing."

"Where did you come from?"

"Macao. My real papa Chinese gambler-man. Mama Russki. Both no good. He sell her. Then he sell me."

There was a long silence.

127

"You're a long way from Moscow," I pointed out to be helpful.

The overhead fan deepened its whirring roar.

"You know *Cages?*" the girl asked me.

Yes, I'd seen The Cages. What about The Cages?

"Is where old man find me."

So the old man had bought her out and now was trying to get his money back.

"How long ago did he take you out?" I asked her.

"Two year," she told me. "First year, me *good* to Old Man. I no tell he steal because he no tell I got no paper. He no tell on me, I no tell on him. *Steal, steal steal.* Custom-Man do too *much* steal. 'Old man,' I tell him, 'you stop steal now; you do too much steal, old man.' Old man no stop. Old man get catched." The girl clutched her hair to mimic the old man's fright—" 'O-O-O, your little daddy gonna get rig-or-ous labor now! O-O-O your little daddy gonna die in jail—O-O-O' "— her eyes, that had been so leaden, came pleasantly agleam at the recollection of the old man's panic—then dimmed with disappointment: "Old man no get rig-or-ous labor. Old man no go to jail. Old man pay. He go free. Then he make sailor-busyness. Old man buy what sailor got—watch, ring, radio. Then old man say, 'You like nice Anglo gel, sailor?' he no ask *me.* He tell sailor—*sailor* say, 'I pay good money for you, Baby'—How you like *that?*"

I couldn't say I cared for it. But I could see how things could be worse.

I waited.

The girl studied me curiously.

"You like short-term?" she asked at last.

I shook my head: no short-term.

"You like long-term?"

I shook my head: no long-term.

128

"**Mama no good!**" She began one of those demonstrations of absent-minded anguish which, by inflicting sufficient misery upon the innocent bystander, permit the anguishee to make plans of his own for the following day. "Papa no good! Me got no paper! Me got no little baby! Me got no *baksheesh!* Me got no home! Me got nothink! You no want short-term, you no want long-term—O! O! O!—You no good too!"

There, I'd done it again. Every time anybody in Asia tried improving his difficult lot, there I'd be throwing my weight against his chances. I was certainly going out of my way to foul people up.

"Old man t'row me out!" she howled.

"Why should he do that?"

I only wondered.

"Because *you* no want short-term, *you* no want long-term, *you* not give poor girl nothink!"

Nobody loves The Good Guys anymore.

"Back to Cages!" she concluded the demonstration. "Me die! You no good. You no *damned* good."

"Whenever things seem to be darkest, honey, is just before they get worse," I consoled her.

She put her head down on her arms and began shaking her shoulders. It was the most theatrical exhibition of fraudulent guilt-placing I'd had put on me since James Baldwin accused me of complicity in the lynching of Matt Parker.

"I was at a ball game in Comiskey Park that night," I'd tried to wriggle out; but when James lays down a charge he *lays* it.

"You were there all the same," he put it right on me— "your Northern indifference triggered the Southern gun. The men who did the lynching merely acted out the will of the white community—and there is no Mason-Dixon line to *that*

129

community. You are as much a part of it in Chicago as any Mississippi sheriff."

"I don't follow you," I had to admit.

"Because you don't *dare* follow," he challenged me.

"Where would I wind up if I did?" I asked curiously.

"By finding that your father and your father's father conspired in the lynching of Matt Parker a hundred years before the lynching."

"My old man came from Indiana," I felt I ought to explain, as James plainly had me confused with somebody else, "and *his* old man came from Europe."

"Europe raped Africa, let me remind you," James informed me.

"You mean we were in on *that* too?" I asked.

"Everyone in the crucible of Western Civilization was in on it," he assured me.

What could I say except that I was *terribly* sorry?

"I'll have to take responsibility," I finally confessed to the lynching of Emmett Till as well as of Matt Parker, "so long as you'll stop denying you set the Reichstag fire." *

The girl had stopped shaking her shoulders. She had a new thing going. She was trailing her fingers down the front of her blouse, smiling seductively; and every time she touched a button the blouse opened a bit wider. This interested me as I thought that if she got the blouse open entirely it would mean she was going to wash it. By the time she had it open

* "The white community," Mr. Baldwin commented recently upon the murder of Malcolm X., "must share the responsibility for this thing no matter who pulled the trigger; for whoever did it was formed in the Crucible of Western Civilization."

And whoever did it was also formed in the crucible of the American Negro community. If that community's claim to equal justice in the company of men is to have validity, it will have to assume responsibility for its own acts. Putting responsibility on Ol' White Massa for every act of violence of our times affords the Negro a convenient cop-out; and also means he wants to hold on to the immunity of being a slave.

I saw that her bra needed washing even more. I took my bottle and stretched out on the divan.

And felt the beat of the city's terrible heat on rooftop, alley, bazaar and wall. The balloon tied to my finger rose toward the blades of the fan as though irresistibly drawn; then swung like a weightless pendulum there, four swings every half-minute.

My watch ticked off the swings and the beat of the fan slowed to the throb of engines hauling deep below-deck. Seamen were coming down the hall but they didn't know which door was mine. Yet they stopped and began whispering just outside.

"He's trying to get the ship in trouble," one began informing on me.

"It isn't any of his business," a half-familiar voice agreed.

Then the whisperers conferred: they were going to come in on me. I tried to waken but could not. Someone was standing in the door.

"The last stitch is through the nose," he announced. His face was bleeding and his cap was afire. It was a matter of life or death that I waken before he touched me and I did.

And heard Baliram's heavy step upon the stair. He came into the room awash with sweat.

The girl had left her blouse and bra on a chair. Baliram saw it at the same moment that I did.

"Did you enjoy my wife's company, my friend?" he wanted to know.

"Where your wife hangs her underwear doesn't concern me," I assured him. "What did you get for the set?"

"I earned nothing for myself," the old man told me—just as my balloon touched the blades and exploded as though exploding his lie.

"I was forced to sell without profit for myself, because I

131

could not risk carrying it around any longer. I'm becoming too well known, my friend. I know you will not let my services go unrewarded."

A tiny fragment of rubber, all that remained of my balloon, drifted downward toward the floor.

"What did you get for the set?" I asked him again.

"Fifty dollars," he lied in his teeth.

"Count it out," I asked him.

He counted out fifty dollars in rupees. Close enough. I pocketed it.

"Not even cab-fare, my friend?" he begged.

I didn't bother to answer.

Passing down the dimness of the hall I was almost past the girl before I discerned her huddling against the wall.

"Old man think I cheat him," she whispered, "old man think *everybody* cheat."

"Well," I asked, *"doesn't* everybody?"

She held her palm out to me.

"Was it you who informed on the old man?" I asked her.

She wriggled her fingers to tell me her hand was still empty.

"Did you?" I asked her; for I really wanted to know. And she wasn't getting a dime *until* she told me.

She nodded her head in confirmation and I put a dollar's worth of rupees in it. She examined the money.

"If you don't give me another dollar," she told me, "he'll hit me."

"Hit him back," I suggested, and turned down the stair. Into the gala day.

July 15th: Port of Bombay
II. Kamathipura

"Do priest kiss priest?" Alina had wanted to know in *The Lion of Kowloon*—"Do men kiss men?"

Between the abounding sensuality of the Hindu and the Puritanism of the Muslim, betwixt one race whose gods are all lovers and one whose God is a celibate soldier, an ancestral conflict is renewed each night in Kamathipura.

The women and girls who stand in stalls, with pitch-black eyes and brows blackened in ash-white faces, looking silently out at the street beneath the glare of sixty-watt mazdas, are merchandise as open to the view of buyers of the night as canned fish to buyers of the day. But the glare overhead keeps them from seeing the faces of those who stand and look.

They hear laughter of men but cannot see who is mocking them. They hear cries of defiance from girls in other cages; sometimes one curses one of the lookers and he swears back at her laughingly.

Other times the laughter comes more lightly by, from areaways where boys wearing earrings wait. By the light of flares that blow upward, like yellow saris in a twisting wind, old men move among them. Kamathipura is less mocking of earringed boys than of imprisoned girls.

For the Koran is terribly hard on a whore. "If any of your

women be guilty of whoredom," it teaches, "then bring four witnesses against them and shut them up in their houses until death do release them." Early Islam simply walled the woman up alive—an unconscionable barbarity it later sternly revoked in order to stone her to death without qualms.

It looked more benignly upon the male sinner and looks more benignly yet: "If two men among you commit the same crime, then punish both, but if they turn and amend, then let them be, for God is He Who Turneth Merciful."

Turneth Merciful is a God who turns on the mercy for men only. From Woman He Turneth Away. Soldiers always give themselves the benefit of any doubt and Islam was a race of soldiers: women are for one thing only and now let's get back to barracks.

Weakness being shameful and Woman being weak, an open contempt of her is one means of feeling oneself a full man; and may disguise the fear of being inadequate. Islam lacked nothing of making a Playboy club in Mecca a going concern except affluence. It was so rich in disdain that there must have been enough inadequacy for everybody in town to have a bunny all his own.

Yet holding Woman in contempt contains the risk that, if you surrender to her, you yourself become contemptible. Holy men who would not harbor in their hearts neither fear of man nor contempt of woman beat the game by sleeping with one another and billing the bit as "Pure Love." And what was pure enough for a priest was pure enough for a general: the process of purification spread down through the rank and file to the flaring areaways of Kamathipura.

The Koran went down before the *Mahabharata*. Yet the Muslim aristocracy maintained its tradition of homosexuality by keeping pages. That these young studs solaced the master's harem as often as they solaced the master can be safely assumed. And that some resisted the master altogether is recorded by a seventeenth-century traveler, Jean-Baptiste Tavernier, telling of a singular occurrence at Patna:

"An officer disgraced a young boy who was in his service. The boy, overwhelmed by grief, chose his own time to avenge himself. Being out hunting with his master, and removed from other attendants, he drew his sword, came up behind the master and severed his head with a single cut. Then, crying aloud he had slain his master, he rode full speed to the governor's house; who placed him in prison. Although relatives of the slain man demanded the page's execution, the sympathy of the people for the boy was so strong that, after six months, the governor pardoned him."

As the Moors, whose deserts had lent them ferocity sufficient to conquer Spain, became so softened when cut off from their deserts that they changed to a race of scholars, so the desert-men of Mohammed were softened by the grandeur and reverence with which the Hindu civilization surrounded womanhood.

The Indian prostitute was not originally, like the Muslim, an abandoned woman, but a dedicated one. The Dēvi-Dāsi was a temple harlot dedicated to the service of a god. When she was married to the god, the marriage was honored by a festival. As a dancing girl the Dēvi-Dāsi served both man and god, and the man who shared her bed shared it with a god. Rather than feeling corrupted by woman, the Hindu felt uplifted.

Prostitution became womanhood organized. The elaborateness and efficiency with which the king of the Hindu state of Vijanagar had set up the establishment of prostitution stunned Abd-Er-Razzak, an ambassador of a fifteenth-century Persian Shah:

"Opposite the mint," he wrote, "is the house of the governor, where are stationed twelve thousand soldiers as a guard, who receive every day a payment of twelve thousand *fanom*, levied upon the receipts of houses of prostitution. The magnificence of places of this kind, the beauty of the young girls collected therein, their allurements and their coquetry, surpass all description.

"Immediately after mid-day prayer they place before the doors of the chambers, which are decorated with extreme magnificence, thrones and chairs, on which the courtesans seat themselves.

"Each of these women is bedecked with pearls and gems of great value, and is dressed in costly raiment. They are all extremely young, and of perfect beauty. Each one of them has by her two young slaves, who give the signal of pleasure, and have the charge of attending to everything which can contribute to amusement. Any man may enter this locality, and select any girl that pleases him, and take his pleasure with her. Each of the seven fortresses contain places of prostitution, and their general proceeds amount to twelve thousand *fanom*."

The proceeds of the holy whorehouses, it would appear, were turned over to the military before midday prayer and spent back in the houses in sacred copulation that same night. If the girls were thus kept content while the state was being protected, everyone shared in the general prosperity, nobody got up before noon and all were too busy screwing after to dissent from anything, is it any wonder that the king kept laughing his head off?

A Portuguese traveler, Duarte Barbaso, perceived, behind this grandeur, a fearful savagery. (It must be borne in mind that he came of a Christian country which denied womanhood to women: either she married for the advantage of her house or was locked into a deathly vise of enforced chastity.)

"Many women," Barbaso reported, "through superstition dedicate the maidenhead of a daughter to one of their idols here; as soon as she reaches puberty she is taken to a house of worship, accompanied, with exceeding respect, by all her kindred holding festival for her as though she were to be married. Outside the gate of the church is a square block of black stone of great hardness of the height of a man, shut in by gratings.

"Upon these oil-lamps burn all night; and they are ceremonially decorated by many pieces of silk that folk outside may not be able to see within. Upon the said stone is yet another, the height of a stooping man; in the middle of which is a hole into which a sharp-pointed stick is inserted.

"The maid's mother takes her daughter, and other kinwomen within the grating. After ceremonies have been performed the girl takes her own virginity with the stick and sprinkles blood on the stones. Therewith the idolatry is accomplished."

How Barbaso found out so much without putting an eye under the grating is a problem only posterity can resolve.

What seems more pertinent is that these idolatrous women knew that the vagina was intended for *use:* an idea which now so completely confounds the American woman that she attaches it to a two-car garage instead. And then can't understand why years of searching for her femininity through analyst's offices end by leaving through the same door by which she came in—except that her husband is less masculine than when she entered. *Wow.*

The correlation between our rising incidence of homosexuality and our increasing indifference to the suffering of others is partially accountable by the proximity of cruelty to effeminacy; these shade into each other because both overvalue pain. And both are rooted so deeply in Puritanism that

137

we have become more tolerant of homicide than lovemaking.

The thirty-eight witnesses to the murder of Miss Genovese were not uniquely worse than any other thirty-eight window-watchers between Schenectady and Sausalito—had a couple been making love on that walk instead of a woman being stabbed to death, there would have been a surge of outraged citizens upon them like buffalo stampeding.

Of the ancestral savagery of India much remains in Kama-thipura; but nothing at all of the grandeur. The tradition of the temple harlot has brought the dēvi-dāsis to the stalls and the sons of the poor to the areaways.

Between the areaways and the stalls, peddlers of ices and toters of pots, seamen going up stairs that lean and other seamen coming down, sellers of condoms and hawkers of gum, riders of bikes between fly-buzzed cafés, taxis, gharries, hay wagons, drivers and bringers, changers and criers, all are borne past the cages in a diffused light lit by occasional flares. And carried on waves of sound now loud, now soft, now far, now near: of rock-'n'-roll from jukeboxes, transistor-jazz amid a thin bleating of dying balloons; and of a doorbell being buzzed again and again and again.

And all move on a tide of cheap perfume pervaded by urine, face powder, onions frying, burning oil and decaying fruit, a sea of smells, scents and odors diverging; then merging into the single smell of thronging humanity.

Between hush-hush whisperings of the night—"*Come to me here you—Papa you give—Short-term-long-term—You-speak-Joe-you-like-nice-boy—Papa-I-show-you-good-place-you-do-what-you-like-Papa*—I heard a whole night-universe begging Americans for their lives.

Between the cold white glow of the stalls and the hotter light of the areaways, I saw a woman coming toward me; whose eyes, I saw, were crossed.

I'd never before been accosted by a cockeyed whore. It was my first time.

We sat down at a rickety table in front of a café that cast a pale blue light. When a boy came out bowing and scraping I ordered tea before he could start saluting.

She would have been passably good-looking but for those incredibly crossed eyes: I mean this girl was *completely* cock-eyed. And wearing a smile so foolish it was pitiful.

"No short-term," I told her, "no long-term." And shook my head with infinite regret.

She shook her head regretfully as well.

Then took my hands as though to read my palms. But, instead, began matching my fingers with hers, finger for finger. When she had ten apiece, and had established that we both had the same number, I cocked my head toward her to see what she had in mind.

She cocked her head at me in turn.

If this kid wasn't demented then she had a going sense of humor.

I stuck out my tongue.

She reddened, rose and was gone in the misty light of Kamathipura. I called the waiter out to pay him for the tea.

"That girl no can talk, sor," he assured me.

"Why can't she talk?"

"Her Papa very rich Arabian, sor."

"Why can't she talk?"

"Her name, Kusum, sor."

"Why can't she talk?"

"She Singapore gel, sor."

"*Why can't she talk?*"

"Japan soldier take her from Papa. When give gel back to Papa, gel no can talk. Japan soldier cut off tongue. Papa no like gel no more. You think she *see* out them eye, sor?"

139

I spent the rest of that night talking to the women of the cages of Kamathipura, of whom many spoke English brokenly. Some spoke not at all, but merely held out a palm.

Several spoke of Kalyani, the woman who'd spoken for them to Ghandi. And who still spoke for them to the continual parade of reforming committees which visit Kamathipura. Men and women of goodwill who come to take count of incidence of the V.D. rate to see whether syphilis is on the rise or declining; to determine the percentage of women who become prostitutes of their own will or by kidnapping; and to determine from what provinces of India these women have come. Because there is nothing to do about Kamathipura except to chase the pimps off the corners for an hour and take a fresh count.

A light rain was falling, as the light of ordinary day was breaking, when I left Kamathipura. Suklaji Street, Falkland Road and Foras Mews were deserted but for a few taxis in which bearded Sikh drivers were asleep at their wheels. Even the pimps had given up. All the café tables had been taken in but one; and at that a woman slept with her head upon her arms.

As I passed her I realized it was my mute and mocking friend of the blue-lit café.

> Idling the night in blue cafés
> Mid roar of cab and cabaret
> Wand'ring the flares of Foras Mews
> The girl Kusum whose eyes are crossed,
> Whose eyes indeed lean each to each,
> Walked smiling among the alien crews.
> Fists matter little to a whore,
> *Baksheesh* matters more.

When doors are locked to all cafés
And morning slants along the street
Sailor and soldier alike have left
And pimps have made a night of it
Then Kusum, after all have gone,
Dreams yet of seamen on the beach.

In a rain that lightly rains regret
Lamps along the long gray street
Bend, wearied out with all-night love
Like cockeyed lovers each to each.

Fists are no matter to a whore,
Baksheesh is what matters more.

July 17th: Port of Bombay
III. Kalyani-of-the-Four-Hundred

When Mahatma Ghandi came to the south of India he was met by four hundred whores of Bombay.

"How may we become good women once more, Master?" their spokeswoman, one Kalyani, asked the Mahatma.

"Go to the spinning wheel, my children," the Master instructed Kalyani-of-the-Four-Hundred.

"How is the wheel to save us, whom the loom has brought such shame?" Kalyani asked The Master.

CAGE 1

Kalyani's parents were weavers. They owned their own looms, upon which Kalyani's parents, her two brothers and herself worked. They also owned their own house.

When Kalyani was sixteen she married a man from Bombay, who did not have living space for a wife. So Kalyani went to live with her mother-in-law until her husband found accommodations.

Kalyani's mother-in-law mistreated her, as she had wanted her son to marry another girl; yet Kalyani could not go back to her own home. So she lived unhappily with her mother-in-law, hoping her husband would soon send for her.

After a son was born to her, an older woman advised

143

Kalyani to take the child to its father in Bombay, and offered to accompany her there as Kalyani had never been to the great city.

When they reached the city the woman took Kalyani to a brothel and sold her for four hundred rupees. Kalyani at first refused to give herself to men; yet she had no choice, for there was no way of getting out of the place. She gave in to the keeper at last.

Cage 2

Seeta was brought up by her widowed mother who worked as a farm hand. She had an easy childhood and was married to a farmer at the age of eleven. After puberty she lived with him for four years and bore him a son. Then her husband died. Seeta lived alone as she did not want to burden her mother.

She worked as a domestic for paid Rs. 5/- per month plus food and clothing. When the other members of the family went out, the master of the house used her sexually. This continued until her mistress found out and dismissed Seeta.

She was now a spoilt woman; she went to Bombay to become a prostitute.

Cage 3

Parvati's parents were very poor. Her father was a porter and her mother a blind beggar. She was the eldest child and had eleven siblings, all younger than herself. With her family she lived in a *Harijan* colony amongst the poorest people. Parvati picked wastepaper, rags, and bones from the garbage pails and sold them. She used to roam the streets alone at all hours. Men took advantage of her. Parvati had sex experience from the age of eight. At fourteen she was happy, with the approval of her parents, to join an aunt in a brothel.

144

CAGE 4

Prema's parents were industrial workers and she was their only child. When the parents were away for work, Prema was left alone. When she was fourteen, Prema fell in love with a lorry driver and eloped with him to Bombay, where they lived together for four years.

The man started drinking and beat Prema every day. She ran away and came to Kamathipura, where she found shelter and an easy way of life.

"We are prepared to take any number of men, but they don't come," Prema now complains.

CAGE 5

Sarasa's family lived contentedly, as they had their own farm and house. Sarasa played a lot with the children of her locality and passed a happy and comfortable childhood. At the age of nine she was married to a farmer. Later, she lived with him. Two years passed happily. Then her husband died of a fever.

Sarasa continued to stay with her in-laws, who asked her to remarry; but she felt that her marriage had been broken by God. So it was no use marrying again.

At eighteen Sarasa returned to her own home. She worked on her father's farm for four years and then she saw women from Bombay who appeared to be happy and well-to-do. So she went to Bombay. At Victoria Terminus a *gharwalli* took her to Kamathipura.

"Why do you make me think of days that are now gone?" Sarasa wants to know.

CAGE 6

Sheela was brought up by her widowed mother, a domestic. Her mother loved her and Sheela helped her mother. When Sheela was twelve her mother died of a short illness. She took up her mother's job.

Sheela fell in love with a young man of her neighborhood and married him at thirteen. Within a few months, her husband died. Sheela felt alone and lost. An elderly woman from Bombay persuaded her to return to Bombay with her, where the woman sold her. At first Sheela refused to work. When she found out she could not leave, she capitulated.

CAGE 7

Anjana's parents died when she was ten. She and her sister started working as domestics. When Anjana was fourteen a man from Bombay showed the sisters sympathy, and they went with him to Bombay; where he sold them to a *gharwalli* for Rs. 500/-. The sisters cried but had to give in.

"Everything is left to God," Anjana believes.

CAGE 8

Usha was the only daughter of a sailor who died when she was ten; her mother was a domestic.

Usha's time was her own, and she spent it roaming with friends. By the time she was eighteen she was completely out of her mother's control. Tired of her incorrigible daughter, her mother no longer cared whether Usha came home or not.

The girl stole some gold ornaments from her mother and went to Madras, where an actor's agent obtained work for her in films, as an extra. He harassed her for sexual favors, but she despised him. She preferred to sleep with a film direc-

146

tor. The agent began threatening her life, and the director no longer wanted her. Usha migrated to Bombay and became a prostitute

CAGE 9

Krishna's father died when she was six and her mother found it difficult to earn enough to maintain the family. The mother used to weep that she could not give enough food to her children. Krishna was married at the age of five, when her father was living, to a grown man who had a mistress. He refused to take the girl when she grew up because he was attached to his mistress. Her mother felt sorry that she could not get her married again because of poverty. Krishna came to know a woman from Bombay who explained to her about prostitution. Her mother gave her permission to go with the woman to Bombay and enter the business "because it is better to live comfortably at any cost than to starve."

CAGE 10

Nancy's parents died when she was an infant and she re-members nothing about them. She was brought up by farm-ers. They gave her enough food and clothes, but treated her like a servant. When she was ten, her guardians left her with a Christian family as a domestic. When her employers left Bombay Nancy was abandoned. She begged on the streets and slept in doorways until she came to windows where women sat with their faces painted. She served as a domestic in a house where most of the women were Chinese. At ten she began accommodating men.

A superstition was then prevalent that a venereal disease could be cured by making love to an under-age girl. By being put to the use of this superstition, the girl suffered several early infections. Although she has now, she claims, effected a partial cure, she has no doubt but that she has infected a number of men.

CAGE 11

Padma was three when her parents died. An old friend of her father, a petty businessman who had no family of his own, brought her up as his own daughter. He was very affectionate toward her and fulfilled her needs till she came of age. She was fourteen when he died.

Padma was left alone. She was attractive to men and was without obligation to anyone. She took up prostitution of her own will, without being seduced into the trade.

"It is just as well not to marry," she feels. "If a woman falls in love with her husband, and is foolish enough to let him detect it, he will deceive her. If she does not fall in love, then she is a slavey. I meet new gentlemen every night, every one of whom swears he loves me. Of course they are all lying. But then that is what I am being paid for—to pretend to believe gentlemen. I would rather be lied to by a variety of gentlemen whom I respect than by a husband I despise."

CAGE 12

Maya's earliest memory was of begging on the streets of a city she now thinks must have been Pandharpur. She remembers a railway station, and of begging through railroad carriages. She remembers a train beginning to move before she could alight and that she was not frightened.

The train came to Bombay and Maya came begging to Kamathipura. She was not yet ten, but a *gharwalli* took her in. She worked in a brothel, as an *ayah,* until she attained puberty. Her *gharwalli* then turned her over to the trade in young girls.

148

"Just you wait," she stands at the bars of her cage and tells men who are passing, "just you wait, you child-killers."

CAGE 13

Girija lived in an abandoned hut and worked for her neighbors to have food. Girija had nobody in the world. She was grateful to a man who came to her and made love, though she was too young to feel or to understand the act. He used her regularly, sometimes giving her money, and was later replaced by other men. One of these brought her to Bombay and sold her for four hundred rupees.

CAGE 14

Indira grew up tending younger children in a missionary orphanage. Her lot was the storing of water and cleaning of floors. She was nine years old when this routine was interrupted by a trip to Bombay. The child was so charmed by the city that she ran away from the orphanage to return there. Since she spoke only Kannada, it was inevitable that the friends she found were the Kannada-speaking women of Kamathipura. She has since picked up a number of other languages.

CAGE 15

Sundari's parents were weavers who owned their own looms. She was an only daughter, and was brought up strictly. At sixteen she married a man from Bombay, but he did not bring her back to Bombay with him as, he claimed, he did not have living accommodations for her. When he finally brought her to Bombay she had to live there with his mother, who mistreated Sundari because she had wanted her son to marry a widow who owned property. Sundari's husband was afraid of his mother.

When Sundari gave birth to a son, the husband's mother began to beat Sundari at will while the husband stood by. The girl came to Kamathipura to avoid more beatings. The husband now visits her house regularly, and regularly pays the housekeeper for the privilege of sleeping with his own wife. He makes love to her passionately, Sundari says. But after he is through making love he reproaches her: "If I had listened to my mother I would never have married you."

Cage 16

Sukla's parents were sellers of toddy, and Sukla was the youngest of several toddy-toddlers. She was married, at ten, to a farm-laborer, and began living with him when she was fourteen.

Six months after her first experience of sex, her husband took a mistress whom he refused to give up, although she begged him desperately not to abandon her for the other woman. To this he responded by refusing to have anything to do with her.

"How can I, a young girl, live without a sex-life?" Sukla thought, and left her husband for Bombay.

She has now been a prostitute of Kamathipura for three years, and confesses to be weary of the love of men. She has not practiced Lesbianism; but has felt herself tempted.

"I cannot say I will not drink of that well," Sukla admits, "sooner or later, of that well I will *have* to drink."

Cage 17

Kamala's father was a mill hand. After her mother died of tuberculosis he married Kamala to a farmer of their native village. Within a year of their marriage she had borne a son to her husband, and he had begun beating her. She carries the scar, on her forehead, of a blow he gave her that knocked her unconscious. When she recovered from this blow she walked out of his house with nothing that belonged to him, carrying her child and wearing only a house-dress, to return to her father.

Her father became wild with her, claiming she had brought a terrible shame upon her family. Kamala left her father's home and has never seen either her child or her father or husband since.

At 4 A.M. the landlord wakens her for his rent of one rupee. At 4 annas per man, this means she has to take four men merely to make the day's rent. Then the brothel owner collects two rupees from her—eight more men. Thus Kamala has to accommodate twelve men before she has enough to buy food.

"A poor life," Kamala says, "but better than no life at all. God has more than He has spent."

CAGE 18

Long before Ghandi came to the south of India, Kalyani was held in a brothel of the lowest order, against her will. But she succeeded in getting a note out addressed to her husband, advising him of where she was being held.

Kalyani's husband came immediately to that place, and fought bitterly (though no actual blows were exchanged) with his wife's *gharwalli*. He finally got Kalyani out of the place by giving the *gharwalli* a promissory note covering Kalyani's debt to the house.

"As I am now deeply in debt," her husband then told Kalyani, "I will put you in a much better house."

He was as good as his word. The house in which he put

151

her, and in which Kalyani remains to this day, is one of the best in Bombay.

But she is still in debt. It is now plain that no spinning wheel will get her out.

This was why Kalyani asked The Master, *"How is the wheel to save us whom the loom has brought such shame?"*

July 22nd: Arabian Sea

Crying hoarse warnings to a soundless sea, the ship slides and dips in the trough of the waters, under a weighted sky. Rail, rigging and deck break out in a cold-clinging sweat: the ship is afraid of the sea.

Two hours out of the Port of Cochin, we are running into heavy weather. Somewhere below, behind ladder or beam, Manning lurks, ready to pounce on contraband.

Chips is the party I'm salty about. He hasn't paid me the fifty he promised to return in Bombay.

I discovered him heaped beneath a G.I. blanket on the fantail, pretending to be asleep. I yanked the blanket off him. He was lying face-down naked to the waist, hugging the pillow, like a man dreaming he's having a woman. I kicked the sole of his big fat foot. He opened one great pale eye.

"I want that fifty in Calcutta," I told him.

"You'll get it when I get a draw," he told me, and shut the great pale eye. He looked like something fished from the deeps that hadn't been slit and hung to dry because the Captain thought we'd hooked something of interest to science.

"I'll get it draw or no draw," I promised him, and walked away.

I went up to the radio shack. The door was shut. Within, the ceaseless jot-jot-jot of Morse code informed me Sparks

NOTES FROM A SEA DIARY

was on the job. When I opened the door he turned his head, headphones clamped, toward me.

"It wasn't any of your business," he told me.

"What business is *that?*" I wanted to know.

He turned back to his work. I knew what he meant alright. He was still salty about my getting between him and Manning to keep him from kicking the man to death. Let him stay salty. I went down to see what the seaborne winos were up to.

Where had I read that seamen had faces bronzed by sun and salt-sea air and that their eyes scanned far horizons? The only horizon I'd ever seen a seaman scan was a clothesline on which damp socks moved in the wind of a small electric fan, deep in the bowels of a ship. Their mugs were the hue of gin except for those who'd been born sunburned.

According to the script, they got homesick in every port. But I'd never seen one hit the beach, with money in his pockets, whose thoughts weren't cutting in closer to the closest whorehouse than to home. Nobody goes for a life on the roving deep whom life on the beach hasn't first made seasick.

Crooked-Neck was the only man in the crew's lounge; he was stretched on his side to favor The Monstrous Boil. A deck of cards was scattered along the mess table. I shuffled them and began dealing myself make-believe draw poker.

"I heard you wrote a poem," Smith began his usual game.

"My trade is writing," I told him defensively.

"Say a poem," he ordered me.

The first hand I dealt held a pair of deuces, a pair of fours and a five. I threw away the five; rather shrewdly, I felt. The strongest hand left was a pair of eights with a pair of aces and a deuce. There goes the first guy's full house, I reflected, and took time out to accommodate Smith.

154

"The Assyrians came down like a wolf on the fold—"

I remembered—

> *"And his cohorts were gleaming in purple and gold*
> *The sheen of his spears was like stars on the sea*
> *When the blue wave rolls nightly on deep Galilee*
> *Like the leaves of the forest when summer is green*
> *That host with their banners at sunset were seen*
> *Like the leaves of the forest when summer hath flown*
> *That host on the morrow lay withered and strewn—*

"That's all I remember," I told him, drew one card face-down, one to a possible straight, one to a possible flush and one to the aces and eights. The first card I turned up was a deuce: well what do you know, a full house with the case card. The other hands missed, every one. I dealt around once more.

"Come again," Smith ordered. I waited till I had five cards to every hand—

> *"They went forth to battle*
> *But they always fell*
> *Their eyes were fixed upon their sullen shields*
> *Bravely they fought, and nobly*
> *But not well*
> *And on the hard-fought field they always fell."*

I looked at my players' hands while Smith thought *that* one over. The first two hands were dead, but the third needed only one diamond to flush, the fourth held three sixes and the sixth hand held four clubs with a pair of jacks. I drew one card to the first hand, kept a king kicker to the three sixes and split the jacks on the last hand. The first hand missed the flush, the trips didn't improve, but what do you know, the club came in to the last hand! Toward morning the farmer gets lucky.

"It goes this way for days sometimes," Smith began to grieve, "then it gets worse. Every time a man tries to do the right thing the world turns against him, sir."

When Smith added a "sir" he was planning a touch.

"Don't try me for a nickel," I warned him, "I won't bend."

"It isn't money on my mind," he complained, "it's the clap. I developed a drip the morning after we went ashore in Bombay and reported it to Manning. He made me promise to pick up the girl I'd been with and take her with me to the company doc."

I kept dealing.

"It took me half the morning trying to find her. She was living with another hooker and they were both friendly girls. But I couldn't come straight out with my story because I didn't want to get my old-lady-of-the-night-before in Dutch.

" 'Do you feel like taking a walk with me?' I asked her. 'No, but if you do, bring back another bottle of rum,' she asked me, and put on an old Johnny Ray record, all about a little white cloud that cried. I began dancing with my old lady's friend.

"I got along *good* with that one. It looked like I had me a new old lady, and my Night-Before-One jumped salty—'We're out of rum,' she told me— 'How about it?' 'Are you coming down to get it with me?' I asked her. 'Get it yourself or blow,' she told me. That made *me* salty.

" 'I have to blow anyhow,' I told her, 'account I picked up a dose off you last night and I'm now on my way to the doc, so put on your hat and come with me unless your mind has snapped.' She came at me like gangbusters. She shoved me halfway down the stair— 'And don't come back!' she hollered after me.

156

"I done the best I could, didn't I?" Smith asked me. "After all, I'm not a Health Officer. Then the company doc tells me to use a condom next time and sends me on my way. I didn't have a thing!"

"So what's your beef? I should think you'd be happy to find out you're not sick after all."

"I *was* happy about myself, but not about bugging that girl about being infected. The only thing I could do was go back and tell her I was wrong. I wouldn't sleep that night if I didn't un-bug her. I went back."

"That was very decent of you, Smith," I told him.

"Wait till I tell you," he cautioned me. "I went back and she was out—maybe gone to her own doctor—and the other girl was just sitting around looking restless. I asked her if I could wait for my Night-Before-Old-Lady and she said sure, and brought out rum and Cokes, and we had a couple of drinks. Then she put on Johnny Ray singing about that little white cloud, and before the cloud had finished crying we were in the sack making it—that girl was wound up so tight it felt like she never *would* unwind. But when she began unwinding she unwound so fast I had to hurry to catch up: it was absolutely The Greatest Lay— Ouch!"

Smith sat up grimacing with pain—he'd shifted onto The Monstrous Boil a moment. Now he shifted off it with such enormous care that, by the time the move had been made, he'd lost the thread of his story.

"Where was I? Oh yes—there we were, absolutely *out*. I had just strength enough left to fall off that girl and she was already asleep when in walks my Night-Before-Old-Lady— '*What the hell is going on here?* Why you clappified double-backing sonofabitch'—she hauled me off the bed, straddled me and began banging my skull against the floor. She would have beat my brains out if she hadn't reached to grab a hairbrush off the dresser so I could tumble her off. I grabbed my pants and shoes and got through the door with her after me with the hairbrush and down the stairs buck-naked. She came halfway down the stairs, pitched the brush and did a U-turn back into the room. I heard the door slam. I put my pants on in the street."

"What about The Greatest Lay?"

"Either she was completely out or just pretending to be. All the while we were battling she didn't stir Inch One. What happened after I don't know, but I don't think my Night-Before-Lady was hot at *her*. It was the idea she had that I was making out when I had a dose, and I didn't get a chance to tell her I had the doc's okay."

"Don't let it get you down, Smith," I consoled him, "we're all human. We all make mistakes."

"We don't all make mistakes like mine," Smith grieved. "I've caught the worst dose I ever had in my life off The Greatest Lay—and all Manning will do for me is give me pills."

"Don't worry," I told him cheerfully, "maybe it's only congenital."

Night in the Gardens of
Horn & Hardart

Hemingway and Lardner

THE god of the Middle Border was a Now-you-see-me-now-you-don't-scratch-my-back-and-I'll-be-back Sporty-O Jehovah, propitiable by prayer. So long as you gave him an hour of hymning on Sunday morning and provided an organ with a heavenward trump, he'd vibrate your soul with an I-Shall-Quit-This-Mournful-Vale sensation then let you sleep it off on apple pandowdy all Sunday afternoon.

A God who wouldn't stick needles and pins in your little ones because you cut a corner or two on a real estate deal. What was wrong with speculation so long as you didn't use your own cash? Long before the Pentagon devised the phrase "military dialogue" the owners of the Middle Border knew there was nothing wrong with any war you didn't go to yourself.

If you didn't make trouble for Him, He wouldn't make trouble for you, this God-of-Good-Dividends who never tossed pebbles at your midnight window just to whisper *"Hey you! He who gains his life shall lose it."* Nor ever tossed a rock through an Oak Park window wrapped in a warning—*"Man shall not live by bread alone, man."*

Hard times on the rivers and hard times on the plains, hard times on the farm and hard times in town, had bred a midland generation of Righteous Grandfathers who'd stayed right with *Him*. And now, by God, Grandpa had the property to show for it.

Risks that were narrow had all been taken; times that were hard were over at last. What was there left to do in the world now for winners except to keep out losers?

"They built high walls, not only about the walls of their houses," Booth Tarkington observed, "but they walled up their associations with one another as well."

Coming from one Righteous Grandfather who owned a good piece of Indiana pandowdy himself, it is curious that Tarkington's observation touches upon that of Chekhov, writing, of Russia's landed gentry, that "there is poverty all around and the footmen are still dressed like court jesters."

For it was not only their homes, and their associations with one another that the winners of the Middle Border walled, but their mills and factories as well. This was not only a means of protecting private property, but also a way of removing their lives from those of the men and women who worked for them. They thus effected a separation of their lives from the life of American multitudes; and subsequently created a dream-world more real to them than the world of struggle going on in the streets. The men that their power and wealth nominated for public office, therefore, were consistently men who prided themselves upon their "practicality."

A practicality as wholly dedicated to keeping their dream-world inviolate as it was to keeping trespassers off their property: they had more success in keeping the violators of property out than in keeping out violators of their dreams.

Among the footmen of literature dressed like court jesters, defending a world in which property and prestige were more real than love and death, were such writers as Tarkington, Clarence Buddington Kelland and William Dean Howells;

162

whose classic comment was that literature should be written for maiden eyes alone.

But American literature has not been made by writing about lives undeflowered. Literature is made upon those occasions when a challenge is put to the legal apparatus by a conscience in touch with humanity.

When the city clerk of Terre Haute refused to issue warrants for arrest of streetwalkers despite his sworn legal duty to issue warrants for arrest of streetwalkers, and instead demanded of the Terre Haute police, "Why don't you make war on people in high life instead of upon these penniless girls?" that little sport performed an act of literature.

For he was sustaining the great beginning Whitman had made when he wrote "there shall be no difference between them and the rest." A beginning marked by an exuberant good humor; that yet sought darkly for understanding of America.

And sought through New York's Bowery and down Main Street of Winesburg to the edge of town; where the last gaslamp makes all America look hired.

A search past 4 A.M. gas stations upon nights when cats freeze to death on fire escapes and chimneys race the moon; down streets that Sister Carrie knew.

Beyond the grandfathers' walls there began to flow a blood-colored current of vindictive life; that was fed into America's heart by violators of the grandfathers' dreams.

These were impractical men who lived upon a street for whom nobody prayed; where the cries of the sick, the tortured and the maimed had gone unheard.

They were the accused with whom Whitman had taken his stand when he wrote "I belong to those convicts and prostitutes myself." Guilty or not guilty, Whitman pled the defense.

As Stephen Crane had taken his place beside Maggie; as

had Dreiser beside Clyde Griffiths. As had O'Neill beside Anna Christiansen; as had Richard Wright beside Bigger Thomas. As had Tennessee Williams beside Blanche DuBois. And where James Baldwin made his still-unanswered challenge: "If you don't know my name you don't know your own."

What these writers shared was the perception that the owners of their society had not only lost touch with one another, but with their own true selves. The youth who had early armored himself against love became the man who found greater gratification in property than in love; the girl who began by evading the touch of the propertyless man became the woman demanding that Robin Hood be banned from the local library. For the prophets and preachers of this midland bourgeoisie damned the basic act of love as piggishness; while dignifying acquisitiveness, if succeeding on a scale sufficiently grand, as virtuous. Thus marriage consummated more for increase of property than for physical gratification seemed, to this strata, to be morally higher.

"When one is peacefully at home," Chekhov had seen what all these impractical men had also seen, "life seems ordinary. But when one goes into the street and questions women life becomes terrible."

It wasn't Tarkington but another Hoosier who heard, below the roar of ballpark crowds with a doubleheader sun striped across them, cries for help from beneath the stands. Ring Lardner left the park laughing strangely to himself. And later sat drinking alone.

Lardner's women come out of that same suburb of hell wherein Eliot's women waited in parlors for husbands with headpieces made of straw. Indeed those splenetic vixens, whom W. C. Fields feared perpetually to confront, occupy the kitchen of the same house. Lardner's marvelous mimicry barely concealed his dread.

Though all his marriages are desperate, and all his women prepare to cry to have their own way, their tears are never from disappointment of the flesh. Lardner's woman weeps because another woman's husband is succeeding faster than her own; because a daughter married beneath her, or because her son failed to make a certain fraternity.

The desolation of her view is reflected by that of Lardner's aging husband looking out the window of a Miami-bound Pullman:

"First we'd see a few pine trees with fuzz on 'em and then a couple acres of yellow mud. Then there'd be more pine trees 'n more fuzz and more yellow mud. And after a while we'd come to some pine trees with fuzz on 'em and then, if we watched close, we'd see some yellow mud."

The God of the Middle Border had avenged Himself. He had let the Righteous Survivors sleep untroubled only to waken to a nightmare: the walls by which men and women had been divided from their true selves now divided them from conscience. The men they named to speak for them were men whose morality was no more than a projection of consciencelessness in the name of a whole class. Saith the pandowdy Jehovah: "If you're well-to-do you don't need a soul."

The heart had been made fat and the ears heavy. They heard but understood not. They saw yet perceived not.

Nada was a sea of yellow mud seen through a Pullman window.

Ring Lardner discerned the myths. He heard the cries. But he didn't know what to do about the lies. In a mock-biography he reported himself as a radio enthusiast who had designed his own set:

"At first he was unable to get any station at all and this

165

condition held good to the day of his death. But he was always trying to tune in on Glens Falls, New York. It was not until his last illness that he learned there was no broadcasting station in that place."

There was no broadcasting station in America. Lardner ended with nothing to tune in on. Hemingway's own set did not begin to work until he was in Paris.

II. Hemingway Himself

The surprising thing, next to their progressive corpulence, is the amount of paper that is scattered about the dead. Their ultimate position, before there is any question of burial, depends on the location of the pockets in the uniform. In the Austrian army these pockets were in the back of the breeches and the dead, after a short time, all consequently lay on their faces, the two hip pockets pulled out and, scattered around them in the grass, all those papers their pockets had contained. The heat, the flies, the indicative positions of the bodies in the grass, and the amount of paper scattered are the impressions one retains.

Out of the scattered letters of that field, Hemingway wrote his own letter to the world.

He wrote to the woman whose life, she had been told, had been complete by having her own checking account. To her, the death of Catherine Barkley brought a fear that she who guards her life too well might lose it. A strange unease surrounded her heart. Was it possible that one had to earn one's death in order to become alive? And should no tragic hour strike for her, would it not mean that her own death would be nothing more than a mere sloughing off into earth of a husk no sun had warmly touched?

And light was all it needed
And a little cleanness and order.

To this woman, watching her husband waving goodnight to friends in his well-lit door, he seemed unaware of that dark precipitous edge whereupon both endured their days and nights together. She had no way of knowing that he, too, was secretly afraid.

What did he fear? It was not fear or dread
It was a nothing that he knew too well.

If an increasing awareness of the precariousness of life is increase of wisdom, the death of Catherine Barkley made this woman wiser. And if the belief she had sustained in an after-life was thereby shaken, it was because her own life began to feel like a sieve through which living hours kept draining.

Hemingway liked to say that he wrote on the principle of the iceberg that has seven-eighths under water for the one part showing above. And how aware he himself was of his own depths can only be guessed.

He knew he had the critics fooled, those who, like Macdonald, swallowed the image put out by one *Esquire* illustrator, depicting him machine-gunning sharks. That he would take a machine-gun to sea is as preposterous as it would be to take a howitzer on safari. That was the image all the same: The Violent American, the man of no memory all muscle and blood, standing with one foot on the head of a slain lion.

Among the critics, only Malcolm Cowley and Maxwell Geismar have perceived that what Hemingway appeared to be—the Byronic reporter of the bullring, the boxing ring and battle—was only the surface of this writer. If he had been no more than this—had he been only the writer who most represented his time—he would never have provoked the attacks of the begrudgers. It was his submerged sources which troubled them so. For he did not represent his time at all: he made his time represent him. Because within him the whole buried burden of America's guilt, the self-destructiveness of a people who felt their lives were being lived by somebody else, found expression.

In a sense of longing and a sense of loss, Hemingway identified himself with the victims of America; as though those most unworthy of love were the most worthy of it.

His sketch, called *A Pursuit Race,* in which Campbell, an advance-man for a burlesque show, wearies of trying to stay one town ahead of the show, demonstrates Hemingway's early commitment to those who resigned not only from war, but from the race for Success.

"I'm hopped to the eyes," Campbell tells Turner, his boss, when Turner finds him under the sheets in a cheap hotel. Then, rolling up his sleeve, Campbell reveals a line of purple-blue punctures from elbow to wrist.

"They've got a cure for that," Turner assures Campbell.

"They haven't got a cure for anything," Campbell contradicts Turner.

Then, caressing the sheet with lips and tongue: "Dear sheet, I can kiss this sheet and see through it at the same time . . . Stick to sheets, Billy. Keep away from women and horses and eagles. If you love horses you'll get horseshit and if you love eagles you'll get eagleshit and if you love women you'll get a dose."

"Are you alright?" Billy asks.

"I was never so happy in my life."

This is not merely a story about drug addiction. It is a report on isolation as an American affliction.

Hemingway came of a strata so afflicted. His great innovation was not the devising of a literary style, but bringing

to this class a realization of what was real and what was un-
real. A realization for which he went back to the Old Testa-
ment.

> *The sun also ariseth, and the sun goeth down, and hasteneth*
> *to the place where it ariseth . . . and there is no new thing*
> *under the sun.*

The reason that the critics failed Hemingway is simple:
they didn't read Hemingway. They read, instead, other critics
of Hemingway.

"I did not try to see behind the façade," an Italian critic
admits with contentment, "nor what view of life was beyond
that depersonalized style. This has been done, however, in
Mr. Savage's essay." He doesn't tell us what critic Mr. Savage
went to to understand Hemingway.

Nevertheless—we have his word on it—that "Mr. Savage
shows how the entire extrusion of personality into the outward sensational world makes Hemingway's characters the inwardly passive victims of a meaningless determinism; how the
profound spiritual inertia, the inner vacuity and impotence,
which is a mark of all Hemingway's projected characters, ends
in a deadening sense of boredom and negation which can only
be relieved by violent, though still essentially meaningless,
activity; how the final upshot of it all is the total absence of
a sense of life, so that life is brought into a sensational vivid-
ness only by contrast with the nullity of death."

I never cease to be astonished when I see someone like this
dealing with half a deck and nobody calling him on it. "The
most essential gift for a good writer," Hemingway told an
interviewer, "is a built-in, shock-proof, shit-detector." Almost
any kind of detector would serve to detect what the above
critic is spreading around.

Another charge the critics made against Hemingway con-

170

sistently was that he was a man who wrote as though he had no memory. And yet it was Hemingway, and none other, whose memory was adequate enough to give new life to John Donne's sermon that no man is an island. For his memory worked in terms of a race-memory; whereas theirs was limited to the dates of their own reviews.

Nor was his style a clever trick, an acquired device that a clever young man, panting to get along in the world, picked up from Gertrude Stein, as Macdonald claims. It wasn't Hemingway who needed to follow Miss Stein around Paris with notebook and pencil poised, but Miss Stein who needed the pencil. His style was the means by which he fulfilled a need uniquely his own; thus filling a need of the company of men.

This need was for light and simplicity. In achieving it for himself he achieved it for others enduring a murky complexity. By strength of his own love he forced a door. That opened into a country in which, for those willing to risk themselves, love and death became realities.

For Hemingway, in his life as well as in his writing, always left a door wide for others to enter.

Robert Frost, at his 75th birthday party, found himself being introduced to Gene Tunney.

"How did it happen that Hemingway bloodied your nose?" Frost asked just that fast.

Tunney took a step back as though he'd just walked into a stiff jab.

"I was trying to teach him something," Tunney remembered, "but you had to watch him every second."

What Macdonald means, in saying that *he* had Hemingway's goat, is merely that Hemingway never considered him a worthy opponent.

Why should he? There's one in every crowd.

171

III. The Real Thing in Kitsch

        I once observed another bearded man trying to force another door: one of those little glass jobs of Horn & Hardart's. In the days when you had either to smash the glass or put in some nickels.

As a man of force, this one might have smashed a lemon chiffon pie without leaving an imprint unless he were using both hands and chocolate would have stopped him cold. He was a critic whose passion for nickels was barely surpassed by his concern for his corpuscles. Precisely, his passion was so corpuscular that, once had he announced himself as "The Diagnostician of our diseased culture," the self-congratulatory tone was justified; as he himself was a charter member of the affliction.

At the moment, this curious fellow had a salad in hand and was trying to get the attention of someone behind one of the little windows. Something had gone wrong at Horn & Hardart's.

The girl who was witnessing this scene beside me was from out of town. She was from so far out of town that she called the place *"L'Automatique."*

"Does your friend have a difficulty?" she wanted to know.

For the Diagnostician of a Diseased Culture had now put his salad down as if it were contagious. He was dissenting from somebody who was behind the window; judging by his expression, his dissent was sharp.

173

"He says that American culture is a pudding of mediocrity," I reported, "if you call that 'a difficulty.' "

Now he picked up the salad he'd put down and tried to insert it into the open window—it shut so fast he had just time to withdraw his fingers. But the fringe of his beard caught and there he was, trapped with a salad in one hand. He was a tall man and he'd been caught bending. He rapped the glass and waved the salad until the window was opened, releasing him. Then it shut. He inserted a nickel. It reopened, he drew out a second salad and returned to our table, carrying both.

Yet he appeared perfectly composed.

"Is it not permitted to make exchange of salads in *L'Automatique?*" the girl asked about the rules.

"When God is dead, *all* is permitted," the critic quoted Dostoevsky contentedly; in a kindly tone.

"Providing one puts in an extra nickel," I pointed out.

He was a critic with a beard that appeared to be more of an appendage fastened with Elmer's Glue-All than anything growing from skin. He was a de-corpuscled diagnostician who preferred riding the subway to taking taxis unless he was pursuing a celebrity. His pleasures were few and riding in a taxi with a celebrity was an experience as rich to him as riding a passenger train.

Bartenders regarded him without enthusiasm because The Dram Shop Act discouraged them from throwing him out. They didn't mind his mixing Coca-Cola and Scotch so much as they did his using half a case of Cokes to one shot of Scotch. Celebrities seldom minded him because they were never sure which one he was.

"What kind of writer is he?" my friend inquired, after the critic had left his two salads for us to guard, pending his return from another visit to the little windows.

174

"A kind difficult to define," I decided, "his field seems to be that of deriding Philistines for exploiting the *avant-garde.*"

"And *do* Philistines exploit the *avant-garde?*" she inquired.

"No. The *avant-garde* exploits the Philistines."

The Diagnostician was now in a dispute with the handle of a faucet that pours a nickel's worth of milk into a nickel's worth of coffee, this combination then being purchasable for a dime.

Assuming that a man who could measure an entire culture could tell at a glance that he'd gotten only nine cents' worth, the faucet was obviously in the wrong.

"Is it not against the rules, exploitation?" the girl asked, eyeing the begoggled wretch suspiciously.

"It is," I tried to bring her up to date—"but they keep changing the rules. It used to be *against* the rules for an artist to become rich. He was *supposed* to live in extreme poverty and remain unknown until he died of exposure. Upon which event his fame would become widespread and great sums would be made out of the beauty found in his paintings or his books or his songs. Now he doesn't have to die to become famous. He doesn't, in fact, have to create a work of beauty. In fact he doesn't even have to be good. All he has to be today is become *avant-garde.*

"You see, so many people have become rich, and so few people are recognized *avant-gardists,* that it is like a country run by electricity where there is a shortage of electricians. There are simply not enough *avant-gardists* to go around.

"So many people have become rich so easily that they can't get enough of books that tell them how rotten they are. This provides a neat way for the *avant-gardist* not only to denounce culture, but to get rich by doing it. And the Philistines are so afraid that someone will catch them *not* applauding, that a writer, like our friend, not only makes money by being

175

against *kitsch* but earns a reputation for being *avant-gardist* too."

"I do not understand this *kitsch*," the girl admitted, "is it the pudding of no plums?"

"Not exactly," I told her. "It is a pudding that *pretends* to have plums. It is any song, or play, or book, or painting, or film that pretends to be profound although it is shallow, and true although it is false."

"Then it is good that your friend is against *kitsch*—is it not?"

"It would be *if* he were. But where *kitsch* comes in, he is the country's widest distributor of it."

"Again I do not understand."

"I will try to be more precise," I promised her, *"par example:* our friend expresses extreme distress at the thing that Hollywood writers do to a good novel, when adapting it to film, which they term 'licking a book into shape.' He claims that what this means is to drain the novel of all reality and offer its corpse on the screen."

"This is a dreadful deed indeed," the girl exclaimed.

"Be patient," I reproached her, "I am still *par-exampling*. Because at this dreadful-deed-indeed called 'licking a book into shape,' no writer in America is more skillful than is our friend."

"I cannot bear to hear more," she whispered in my ear.

"Try all the same," I asked her, "you will be fascinated by its unimportance."

I was keeping an eye on our Diagnostician—whom we shall henceforward refer to, Dear Reader, simply as 'Macdonald,' as that is shorter than 'Diagnostician'—and saw he was now tied up in an argument with the woman who changes quarters into nickels. I assumed he was trying to get six.

"Par example": I continued, "during the Spanish Civil

176

War an American actor named Flynn arrived at the Spanish border accompanied by his studio's publicity department. He was photographed in a Spanish Republican militiaman's uniform, being greeted by a Spanish Republican militiaman, and the photograph was sent to newspapers all over the world with the story that the actor was now fighting against Facism. When the stunt was over he returned to his yacht, anchored in French waters, and had a party."

"I am disgusted with your Flynn," the girl assured me.

"Don't bother," I suggested. "For one thing, he is dead; and, for a second, he wasn't *my* Flynn."

"Then what is the point of telling me?" she wanted to know. She was a child of a strong curiosity.

"The point is that when Hemingway became just as dead as Flynn, and Macdonald made it his business to sum up the man's life, it wasn't necessary for him to compare Flynn's adventure in Spain with Hemingway's in order to create the impression that there was no difference. The picture of Flynn fighting Fascism by shaking hands with a Republican militiaman and that of Hemingway doing the same thing, made it necessary for Macdonald only to comment about how much Hemingway loved being photographed.

"*Kitsch* is a way of implying when one lacks the courage to speak directly. He thus created an impression that Hemingway, too, was faking. All he omitted was that Hemingway was on the Spanish front, in the worst part of the fighting between Madrid and Barcelona for two years. All he omitted was that Hemingway endured battle, wrote the best dispatches on the fighting, assisted on a movie called *Spanish Earth* and, later, wrote a novel about that war which brought the necessity of defeating Fascism in Spain to multitudes in America."

177

"What was the pudding-man doing at that time?" she wanted to know.

"An excellent question," I congratulated her, "he was discovering a way to be a dissenter against the way we live and at the same time to earn good dividends."

"How is *this* done?" she asked me.

"I'm *trying* to tell you," I scolded her—"it is done by being extremely careful about disapproving of the society in which one lives while at the same time being *very* angry at its art. By doing this one is not at all likely to be subpoenaed by a Congressional Committee asking what organizations one belongs to. Congressmen do not consider organizations of intellectuals to be dangerous. In another country, yes. Not here. Here it is the men who organize unions that must be watched. And by knowing this, Macdonald is able to be against things as they are in *Dissent* and for things as they are in *Encounter,* and to make as much money by saying things *against* them one week, as he does by taking them all back the next. This he has learned from watching Hollywood writers lick a book into shape. Only he goes farther—he knows how to lick a *writer* into shape."

"He sounds terribly confused," the girl observed.

"On the contrary," I insisted, "he is very clear-headed."

"But does not this kind of process have a poor effect on the writing of the *avant-garde?*"

"It leaves the *avant-garde* with no distinction between themselves and the Philistinism except to change their own name to 'hipsters' and that of the Philistines to 'squares.' And makes it possible to have both garlic dressing and roquefort."

"In the pudding of mediocrity," the girl said thoughtfully —and this was a most thoughtful girl—"I think Macdonald is no plum."

178

At which moment the Diagnostician materialized beside us with a face full of explanations.

"I didn't mind paying the extra nickel," he advised us, "but I prefer roquefort to garlic and it looked to me like an even trade." He drew the salads closer, for purposes of comparison. "How do they look to you?"

I failed to see the trap.

"Frankly," I told him, "the garlic salad looks better."

Immediately he put it in front of me. "I can't eat both," he assured me, "it's only twenty cents."

Had it not been for wanting to make a strong impression on the girl I *might* have pushed it back. Instead, I found a twenty-five-cent piece and handed it to Macdonald.

He pocketed it and evaded my gaze while a triumphant flush rose in his cheeks at the realization that he had recouped the difference in price between garlic and roquefort.

Only he hadn't. I fixed him with an eye so steely that at last he reached into a small dime-store wallet, unhooked a brass clasp and brought forth a nickel.

He ate the roquefort with a disappointed air. And left us, immediately after, with the same aura of silent reproach. There was no doubt we were both *kitschers* now.

Yet I could not help but marvel at what I had seen: a man recognized as an arbiter of literary style who himself did not possess ordinary grace sufficient to see him through a meal in an Automat.

"In *L'Automatique*," my friend observed after he had left, "*all* seems *automatique*."

Well, I *told* you she was from out of town.

July 25th: Bay of Bengal

"Never let a woman get so worldly-wise that she loses her leadership," Smith glanced up at me from the table where he'd been shuffling a beat-up deck, "I took a seventeen-year-old bum named Gracie and made a fast-stepping queen out of her, but she lacked leadership. The minute you let a woman feel she don't need you to lean on, she's off and away."

"What's our next port?" I wanted to know.

"Calcutta. Gracie got so near to perfect I changed her name to Old Faithful. She kept herself that clean, and kept our apartment that neat, she cooked so good, and done whatever I told her without asking questions, and all the while bringing in five hundred to seven-fifty a week, I had to belt her now and then for being *too* perfect—what else *was* there to belt her for?"

"Was she good-looking?" I asked.

"The doll of the world. One hundred and four pounds of redheaded ravishment, that was all."

"You should have married her," I suggested.

"The truth of the matter is, Mister," Smith assured me, "was that taking out papers on Gracie was *exactly* what I had in mind. When a hustling woman has had as many chances as Gracie had to put me in the pen and didn't, she deserves to work out of a home instead of a bar."

181

"How's your boil?" I inquired.

"You see, I owned the bar Gracie was working out of—and it wasn't a bar—it was a taproom."

"I didn't know there was a difference," I admitted.

"You would if you had to run one in Santa Vaca," Smith informed me, "where all the bars had to shut down at twelve o'clock but a taproom could stay open till four. That made a difference when a ship was docked in town. That was why I called my place *The Fantail*—like it was someplace you just hung around off duty. I know you think I'm a bum, sir, but that's only because you met me at sea. On the beach I'm a first-class operator and I know my trade."

"Every time I talk to you you have a new trade," I had to point out to him.

"I had a three-piece combo going for me, and the drummer had one of those rubber deals we used to slip over a gearshift for when things got out of hand. The piano player wore knucks. The trumpet man was unarmed because he was a sissy. Gracie kept a pound jar of Pond's cold cream in her handbag, and we had an old spade called Bull who took care of the men's room. Bull was very dignified and wore a high white collar and tie, but I never called on him except in ex*treme* emergency because he was on probation and hadn't ought to be working where liquor was sold. We were *ready*."

Smith began that slow rotation of his skull which betokened inner agitation.

"I left the joint early one night—about twelve—and left Gracie in charge. It was breaking daylight when she came in. I was in bed. She put eighty-five bucks on the dresser. Then she took off her slipper and put two c-notes on top of the eighty-five.

" 'Where're *they* from?' I asked her.

" 'A new trick,' she told me.

182

" 'I didn't notice him—he must have come in after I left,' I told her.

" 'No, he was there when you left. The Bosun's Mate,' she told me.

" '*Him?* I asked her. '*Him?* Where would *he* get two bills to blow so free and easy?'

" 'I don't know, Daddy,' she told me, 'but the man is ready to beat.'

" 'You don't know where the money is from but you think the man is ready to beat?' I tried her.

" 'Not if *you* don't think so, Daddy,' she told me, coming into bed.

"I let her go to sleep. I didn't mind beating a Bosun's Mate but I didn't want to undertake whipping the American navy. What if it were ship's funds the man was spending?

" 'I don't want you to rap to that new trick,' I told Gracie the first thing in the morning. 'Don't even say "hello." '

" 'Whatever you say, Daddy,' she agreed.

"Things never start the way you think they're going to. Gracie shook the Bosun's Mate off, wouldn't even drink with him, and he left without a beef. After he left I relaxed because, what I hadn't told Gracie, the reason I was scared of the man wasn't that he might be a thief so much as I was afraid he *might* be law. I was sitting there with a couple old-time hookers, thinking about this move to myself, when one of the hookers says, of a sudden, 'All I want to do is get married.' 'What in God's name you hangin' around *here* for then?' I asked her. 'To give the joint a little class,' she answered me. 'You wouldn't add class to a geek-show,' I let her know, 'every time you come in that door the joint is brought down.' 'In that event I'll leave,' she jumps salty. ' 'N don't come back'—I threw that in just to speed her on her way and she stops dead at the door— 'Just for that last crack,' she tells me. 'I *am* coming back.' 'We'll wait,' I let her know, not worrying about a thing.

"It wasn't half an hour before the door flies open and in comes a flying wedge of so many seamen I thought the S.S. *Idaho* must be in port—at least forty of them lined up at the bar and here comes the Bosun's Mate—250 pounds of him in new whites acting like he never been in the joint before.

" 'Who's the head-pimp here?' he wants to know, coming directly to me to put that question.

" 'I am,' I told him, 'you looking for work?'—and he slugged me so fast I went ass over teakettle and landed against the bar.

" 'And now,' he tells me while I'm still sitting there trying to clear my head, 'we're going to wreck this joint.'

" 'Let me lock the door,' I asked him, 'and we'll help you wreck it.'

"I made it through that mob of sailors to the door, even though my head was still swinging from that sock he give me. I got the door locked. Then *we* went to work.

"I wrapped myself around one of the Bosun's arms, the drummer got the other, and the sissy rapped him with the gearshift-cover. The man didn't even shake. 'I'll kill you a hundred times!' the sissy hollered, and rapped him again. He shook, but didn't go down. 'Give *me* that thing,' I told the sissy, and I brought that rubber down flat on the man's skull. But he didn't go down.

" 'Let *me* try,' the drummer asked, and I handed the rubber to the drummer. He tried it from the back on the very point of the man's skull. That worked better. The man went down.

"But he got right up.

" 'Get Bull,' I told the sissy.

"Bull came out in his high collar and tie, grasped the situa-

184

tion and made a sign for us to step aside. Bull backed up a few feet, then came on skull first right into the Bosun's middle. The man made a sound like *Wuff-ooooof* and went down doubled up. Then we went to work on the others.

"By the time the shore patrol got there we had fifteen sailors laid out. The rest had fled. The Bosun's Mate had come to, but all he could do was sit in the middle of the floor and hold his middle.

The next day the navy hung an OFF LIMITS sign on us. I was as good as out of business. I went to see the Commandant.

" 'Sir,' I told him, 'I've served my country's armed forces too.'

" 'What has that got to do with it?' he asked me.

" 'Sir,' I tried another tack, 'I realize we hospitalized one or two of your men.'

" 'Six of them are still in traction,' he told me, but I think he was exaggerating."

Danielsen came in wearing that lonesome smile; without saying what he had in mind in coming down to the crew's lounge.

"No game tonight," Smith told him, "the guys aren't taking another draw until we hit Calcutta."

Then, since Danielsen merely stood there smiling wanly, Smith concluded his wandering tale.

"I was shut down for twenty-three days. Gracie had to start working out of a joint called *The Club Gayety*. I went to see the Commandant every day. 'I'm sorry as can be, sir,' I'd tell him, 'that we put your men in traction. But, in a manner of speaking, sir, you have *me* in traction too. I can't move either.'

" 'In that case we'll take you out of traction when my men get out,' he told me.

" 'But that may be weeks,' I beefed.

" 'Might be months,' he told me.

" 'I'll be out of business by that time, sir,' I told him.

" 'Your old lady will help make ends meet,' he tells me— just like that.

" 'Can we leave her out of this, sir?' I asked him.

" 'Well,' he tells me, sitting back comfortably in his big navy chair, 'you *are* a pimp, aren't you, Smith?'

" 'I'm not sure what you mean by that, sir,' I told him, staying cool as possible. " 'I run a bar where seamen come looking for women and I don't stand in the way of their wishes, that's all.' "

Smith glanced at Danielsen to see whether the man had decided what he wanted; but all Danielsen did was to smile remotely.

"You see," Smith addressed himself once more to me, "I realized that what the man was doing was trying to provoke me. He was being straight-on insulting so I'd flip and try to slug him, only I didn't flip. I set myself to let anything he said roll off me.

" 'O,' he tells me, 'I *beg* your pardon—I thought one of them redheaded whores was your wife.'

"That *almost* did it—but not quite. I felt my throat go dry and felt my face burning. But I gave him a kindly smile all the same.

" 'Sir,' I asked him, gentle-like, 'has it ever occurred to you that any one of us *might* have been the Christ Child?'

"He lost color because he hadn't expected me to turn sweet on him. Then he started getting red. I saw it was the moment to reach him.

" 'I'm afraid my wife will leave me if we don't get the place open soon, sir,' I told him—and got out of there fast.

The next day the shore patrol came by in a jeep, took down the OFF LIMITS sign, gave me a paper to sign releasing the navy from any legal responsibility, and wheeled away."

186

"You and Gracie must have had a ball *that* night," I surmised.

"It wasn't merely a ball," Smith assured me—"it was a *celebration*—only Gracie wasn't there."

"Gracie wasn't there?" I asked, with the uneasy feeling I've been had again.

"O no," Smith assured me lightly, "she took off with the Bosun's Mate. Like I told you—never let a woman get so worldly-wise that she loses her leadership. Always remember that you can always treat a woman too good—but you can never treat one too bad."

"Look, Smith," I had to protest, "you got a boil on your ass as big as your mouth and you got plates in your mouth that don't fit. You owe everybody aboard and you've got chronic clap. Manning has your discharge papers ready to hand to the company as soon as the ship hits Long Beach and who do you think is going to give a man in your condition a job? You are absolutely the most-fouled-up man I've ever known on land or sea and the worst of it is you don't even seem to know it."

Smith hitched his neck a notch outward to indicate he was giving serious reflection to my reproach.

"You left something out, sir," he told me after a minute, in the humblest voice I'd ever heard him employ—"my wife is in and out of the loony-bin like a fiddler's elbow. Every time I send her an allotment the neighborhood winos take it out of our mailbox, sign it with her name and cash it. The poor thing is lucky if she gets a bottle out of it for herself. I can't do anything about it because my sister-in-law has a rape warrant out on me. And you understand that anyone with a chest as weak as mine can't afford to get into violent situations—to see my brother again would be to risk tuber-

187

culosis. Could you let me have five dollars till I get my draw in Calcutta, sir?"

I found myself examining my wallet and, finding it had nothing in it but a ten-dollar bill, showed it to Smith in order to prove that I didn't have five to loan him.

"I'll be right back with your change, sir," I heard him say and noticed that I wasn't holding the tenner anymore.

"What did he mean?" Danielsen asked me.

"Mean by what?"

"By saying that any one of us might have been Christ?"

"Your guess is as good as mine."

Danielsen turned to leave, but I had a question of my own. He waited.

"Sparks told me that when a sailor is buried at sea and the ship's carpenter sews him up, the last stitch goes through the nose. Is there anything to it?"

"An old sea-tradition still faithfully observed," Danielsen assured me, and again turned to leave.

"*Why?*"—I stopped him—"*why?*"

"Your guess is as good as mine."

That irritated me.

"What the goddamn hell is all the stupid *secrecy* about?" I demanded to know. "You're the fourth man I've asked and everybody ducks like I'm asking a woman about her wedding night or something. There *has* to be a reason."

"There is," Danielsen told me, but lowering his voice and regarding me somehow remotely: "Seamen live between water and land and belong to neither, their whole lives. They can't rest at sea and they can't get rest on land. So they get to thinking that, after death on the ocean bottom, they'll rest forever. But if a dead man's nostrils are left open, he'll take in too much water to get all the way down. He'll float, as he

188

has in life, between bottom and top and never rest for all eternity."

"You're putting me on," was all I could think to say.

The change in Danielsen startled me. It looked like genuine anger. I'd never seen even the hint of that in him. Then his color returned, and he left without a word.

"They'll like me in Calcutta," I assured myself.

The Quais of Calcutta

A LOW half-moon came nodding toward our rigging; then nodded quietly away. A moon at rest, half-wearied yet uneasy, returned and still retreated. A moon for payday lovers, regretting passion spent.

Deep below-decks the seaman lies; whose whore sleeps well in Pusan or Kowloon. The orange-red lamp that lit his pleasure in Ho-Phang Road, burns for another seaman's joy tonight. Seaman who sleeps not well below: the moon is on the beach and broke again.

The tides of night still promise love from all earth's Bamboo Alleys. Women wait, in places called *Club Frisco* and *Sam's New York Bar,* for youths from Denver, Philly and The Bronx. All seas swell with women's longing, ceaselessly. Great fish are sleeping on the waters.

While the moon wanes slowly to ash-white.

Dock-hawks, pretending to be owls, followed us upriver; till our rigging severed the night's last star.

A smear across a dungsmoke pall became the ordinary day.

And dogs of those quais never bark but run away.

Then cowdung cooks, where their barge-fires burned beside our hull, blew smoke across our rails and readied for their day. We tied into a jungle of masts and jutting spars.

193

Whatever they were cooking was too pungent to be fried eggs: that had just occurred to me when the mad head of Crooked-Neck Smith, crowned with hair like feathers afire, thrust itself eye-level to the passenger deck; where it had no business being thrust. Seeing me he came up all the way; his head only one notch awry.

"Notice anything conspicuous about me?" Smith wanted to know.

His shirt, transparently thin, was jutting with contraband.

"Nothing but two cartons of Pall Malls," I told him, "the other looks like Chesterfields."

"Man!" Smith feigned astonishment, "how old are you?"

"Past fifty," I had to admit.

"And with the eyes of a twenty-year-old Cheyenne!—God, I bet when you were *my* age you could see right *through* people!"

"I can still see through you," I let him know, "I won't let you have a dime."

"How about ten bucks?"

"Not ten cents and not ten bucks either."

"You doubt I'm good for it?" Smith's tone accused me.

"No doubt whatsoever. I *know* you're not good for it."

Smith's head jerked half a notch out: he was getting hot. Then he decided he'd just be hurt.

"I can borrow from any man aboard this ship, sir. You *know* that. But as you're our only passenger I wanted to give you first crack."

"I don't deserve it," I told him, "give my chance to Manning."

"Smith," Manning came bellowing down-deck as though he'd been called—"Smith! *Don't move!*" But Smith was already to the ladder. Manning watched him skipping down.

"You're going to get this ship in trouble, Smith!" Manning

194

warned him, then stood looking down at something on the dock. I went over and looked too. It was a young Indian woman in dirty robes, hair matted and eyes sunken. She held one palm upward toward us.

"Papa!" she pleaded, "you give!"

Both Manning and I stared at this sight of living starvation: and living starvation stared back at Manning and me.

"Don't call *me* your papa," Manning called down—"I'm not *your* father."

And when I looked at him he was ashen-pale.

I recall tossing a coin onto the dock and seeing a uniformed guard bearing down on the woman to take it from her. When I looked at Manning again his color had returned.

"Caught Chips with nine cartons," he reported to me briskly, "three Camels, three Old Golds, three Kools."

"Congratulations," I told him.

"Seamen *never* learn," he explained, "just because Customs is soft in one port they think Customs is soft everywhere. I have to protect them from themselves."

Glancing across his shoulder I saw four white-uniformed men drive onto the quai. The only officers who wear white in India are customs cops. As I watched, another car, with four more, joined them. All eight waited in the cars. Manning turned to see what was transfixing me.

"What are *they* up to?" I heard him ask himself.

"Waiting to come aboard," I told him as though nobody else could possibly have guessed.

Manning took off his officer's cap and began running a finger around its sweatband.

"They usually only send Sirdar," he complained.

"Who's Sirdar?" I asked, but he didn't answer.

I left him running one finger around and around his hat.

195

I found Concannon half stripped at his mirror and preparing to shave. A pair of new whites lay on his bunk.

"Accentchuate the positive," he was singing or bawling— *"Ee-liminate the negative/Latch on to the affirmative—"*

Sparks was feeling better.

"Going ashore, Sparks?" I inquired.

"Not *about* to stay aboard."

"You're going to be delayed."

Concannon went to the rail, took one look and began pitching bottles and cartons into the depths of the receiving set that ran the length of his shack. In its vasty deeps he had receivers hidden within receivers.

"I once crammed a little whore in here—she was cramped but she came out okay. All she needed was a shower. Paid her extra. Now," he paused, "was that in Macao or Saigon?" Then he remembered our transistors.

"Get those sets," he commanded me, and I was off straight down into a hell of boilers, pistons and furnaces, barometers and engines, that got hotter and deeper as I descended. At the bottom of that broiling pit I took one moment to look up, down, and all around lest Manning be lurking behind a boiler. We'd hidden the sets behind a red warning: DANGER: HIGH VOLTAGE. I began the ascent, with two sets under each arm, two steps at a time. By the time I reached the deck I was pouring sweat.

The deck was clear. I made the run to the radio shack— followed in by Smith, breathing as hard as I was.

"I only followed you halfway down," he apologized. "I was protecting you against Manning."

What Smith was after was a place to hide his own contraband. Concannon took his cartons and dumped them after our transistors.

"Stay away from Smith ashore," Concannon advised me.

196

I went to the officer's lounge to see what was happening.

The customs cop questioning the Captain seemed to sense that Karensen couldn't afford to lose another ship.

"Your ship has a bad name, Captain." His accent was Oxford.

"I don't gather your meaning, sir," Karensen answered.

"No meaning was intended for your gathering. That your ship has a bad name is a mere statement of fact." He paused. "You are now free to deny the statement."

Karensen wiped sweat off his face. The more he wiped the more he sweated.

"I deny the statement," he said at last.

The officer shoved a paper in front of Karensen, turning it around so he could read it.

"Five," the officer announced, and took the paper back.

"Five *what?*" I inquired from where I stood.

"I beg *your* pardon?" the officer asked me.

"I wondered five what," I answered.

"Who are you?" he wanted to know.

"A passenger."

"Would you mind waiting outside until we are ready for passengers?"

Across the rail the lamps of Calcutta shone through a curious haze: the city burned like sacrifice lit by a memorial light.

When Karensen came out he looked miserable. I returned to the lounge and handed the officer my passport.

"Did I ask you to show me that?" he inquired coldly.

"Come to think of it, you didn't," I admitted, and replaced it in my pocket.

"Will you sit down?" he asked me.

I sat.

"May I see your passport?"

I took it out and handed it to him once more.

Then, after examining my declaration: "Where is your typewriter?"

"Which one?" I boasted, "I have an electric and an un-electric."

"There is only one declared here," he went for it.

"I didn't bring the electric. I was afraid India wasn't ready for it."

"Where is the other?"

"In my stateroom."

"May I trouble you to bring it here?"

I went up to my stateroom, returned with the machine, placed it on the table before him without opening it. As soon as I did he was going to tell me he hadn't asked me to open it.

"*Would* you mind opening it?"

I was pleased to do so.

"Would you mind closing it?"

I was pleased to close it.

"Your passport will be returned to you before the ship sails," he promised.

Going down the ramp with my typer banging my knees I ran head-on into another high-minded, bullet-headed official.

"Where going?"

"Ashore."

"Has been *in*spected?" He pointed to the machine.

"Yes."

"Show certificate of *in*spection."

"I wasn't given any. You can inspect it yourself."

"Is not my duty to inspect."

"What do you want me to do?"

"Get certificate."

I hauled the damned box back up to my stateroom and came back down the ramp without it. Now the only move he had left was to stop me because I *didn't* have a typewriter.

198

He let me pass reluctantly. What they've failed to learn from the British about soldiering, these people have more than made up for in snobbery.

Danielsen, the loneliest-looking sailor since Alexander Selkirk, waited on the dock clasping one wrist with the other; as if trying to keep from arresting himself. His usual aspect was that of a man with the blues. I noticed he was now carrying a full set. For his voice, normally a whisper, was now lowered to a mere movement of the lips. Things that always went wrong with him had now gone even wronger: the customs cops had come on him while he was dressing, found three twenty-dollar bills on his bed, and snatched the lot. He was dead flat broke in Calcutta.

"Why didn't you declare your money?" I asked him.

"Because it worries me for people to know how much I'm carrying," was his peculiar explanation.

"I promise not to tell anybody you're broke," I tried cheering him up.

When I loaned him fifty, joy shook him so powerfully that he gave me a barely perceptible nod. Then he dodged to one side to let a beggar pass. You're supposed to shove them out of your way. Danielsen just wasn't made of the stuff that makes great empires.

"If you let the gate cop take that fifty off you, you might as well go back to the ship," I threatened him.

The gate cop stood beneath beacons so bright that it looked a simple matter to slip past him in the darkness behind the beacons. But he had a gun on his hip, even though no Indian soldier has yet hit a target smaller than a cow from further than four feet, this one might be just lucky enough to have a bullet ricochet off a buffalo and kill us both with a single shot. He decided to capture Danielsen first, as the most dan-

199

gerous-looking, and escorted him to a dimly lit shack to be examined by one final bureaucrat.

I stood outside and watched Danielsen's papers being examined, stamped, restamped, and his passport re-examined, restamped; until at last he was dismissed and came out shaking his head as if he'd just been robbed and insulted again.

I entered and showed my shore-pass but did not so much as lay it on the desk.

"That's all," this one informed me quickly.

"That's *all?*"

"Yis"—and began a smile so downright fawning that I thought he was going to his knees— "Yis. You *gentleman.*"

Well what do you know. I was tickled pink.

"You didn't take long," Danielsen observed as we finally got into Calcutta.

"Because *I'm* a gentleman," I reminded him.

He smiled so wanly I knew I'd made a wildly hilarious joke.

"What are our plans?" I asked him, when we'd gotten into the cab.

"Ezekiel's," Danielsen instructed the driver.

*

Tribesmen through endless Chinese ages, by foot and by horse, fought across the wastes of Asia down to the plains of Assam. What frozen heights, what burning valleys, what marshes, flights, descents and pursuits they endured, achieved this ultimate victory: their good-looking daughters boarded trains to get into a Calcutta cat-house.

Welshman, Cockney, Scot and Irisher, nobly volunteered to help the British put India under their Queen. Sikh and Hindi, Ghat and Gurka, had to yield or serve: simply to bring forth a new tribe on earth even loopier than the tribes that had come before. An estranged race, as unrooted in India as

200

in England; detached from Calcutta and Southampton both: congenital expatriates called Anglo-Indians.

Nonetheless I remain enormously gratified by the concern of Sikh and Mongol footmen, Scots Guards, Welsh Grenadiers, Irish Cannoneers, Cockney cavalry and litter-bearers from Wessex, in preparing a field of lovely girls a full furlong long for me, some dusky as twilight with green half-slanted eyes, dressed for Eighth Avenue if not for Fifth; as well as those of rosier flesh, with hair dark blond or orange-red; dressed in the robes of Kashmir and Bengal. Who had told these kids I was coming?

Somebody must have because not one was missing. Between the bar and the bartenders, a three-piece combo and an air of haste, a welcome-home party was in progress for me at Ezekiel's; the classiest abyss in Calcutta.

Its class derives not merely from the profoundly bad taste of its décor and its genuine phoniness, but also from its practice, unique in Calcutta, of serving Scotch to patrons requesting Scotch and bourbon to those preferring bourbon, without watering either. When you ask for English gin you get English gin and not Indian gin, and nobody puts knockout drops in it in order to rob you later. You make your own arrangements for that.

Between the tables and the bar a pushing throng of seamen and whores, the seamen all drunk and the whores all sober, lent such a cheerful, homey air, what with a brawl of two jolly Englishmen trying to kill one another on the floor, I didn't see how anyone could help but be happy here. The scent of cheap whiskey mixing with cheaper cologne lent a woodland tang to the air, like early fall in Miami when rye-bread trees throw out their first dark blooms. A seaman wearing a single earring pinched me and I would have seized him by his hair, but he was bald. The friendliness of the people and the air conditioning made me feel like going for a little stroll; which I did simply by shoving people aside.

The air is conditioned, the drinks expensive, the women good-looking: and the drop from booths to brothels so fast that any of these women might have a gala night and yet be over the edge the night after.

Over the edge and down is an easy drop, where everyone lives on a ledge. It's only a bit more sudden for her, and only a bit more steep, than it is for the red-collared bellboy, leaping for tips on the red-plush rugs of the Grand Hotel: let a desk clerk catch him picking up a few rupees changing money on the side and it's back to the walks, but leave your little red collar behind.

Calcutta is the place, whatever your job, where the drop is steepest; and the drop from the bars is steepest of all: always some babyface never seen before hustling your tricks before your eyes. And just that fast the knowledge comes: you're waiting for men other women don't want.

The darker women of Ezekiel's seem less estranged than those of the Anglo strain. The girls from Assam, Nepal and Kashmir belong to themselves because they belong to India. But, despite her Indian robes, the Anglo who feels she truly belongs to Essex or Oxford or Kent, belongs neither to India nor to the West. She belongs only to the seaman who mounts her.

That's how it is in The Orient, men. That's how it *really* is.

A tug on my sleeve turned me to face an Anglo in Western dress, her reddish-blond hair worn long; and her eye-shadow trying to hide the tiredness of her eyes.

"See that bloody nay-gur?" she confided—"the very nerve of 'im—awskin' me to drink with the like of '*im*. O, I thanked '*im* like a lydy— 'Thank you ever so kindly all the same'—

but would you mind sitting by me here so's he won't come back—there's a good chap. Bartender! Two whiskeys straight!"

I'd heard fake-cockney spoken before, but this one went at it as though she'd been listening to Audrey Hepburn.

She kept on and on about that "bloody nay-gur" until, turning my head from her, I found myself eye-to-eye with a woman whose eyes were warm with light. Her hair, piled high, was so black it had a bluish sheen. One of the dusky kind of a country I could not place.

"Of what country are you?" I asked her.

"I am of Assam. We are a hill people."

"Your name?" I asked.

"Martha."

"Can you leave here?"

"Cannot now."

"I'll wait."

She shook her head: no, that wouldn't do. Instead, she took a stub of a pencil from her handbag and wrote, on the inside of a book of matches:

Martha. Kanani Mansions. Apt. 872.

"You come there midnight," she instructed me, swung herself off the stool and slipped away into the mob of milling seamen.

"Now there's some say a nay-gur's all one and the same, but how *I* were brought up—" the red-haired monologist's voice kept turning like a barber's pole, stripe after stripe, getting nowhere at all. I decided to walk back to the ship and show up, around midnight, at Kanani Mansions.

*

This was in that twilit Indian hour when bazaars are shadowed and beggars rest.

The voices of Calcutta, that great city, change then from

the loud cries of the workaday world to murmurous pleas of evening. Nobody knows how many people there are in Calcutta.

Nor how many cats died yesterday there.

Nobody knows how many cats were born in Calcutta yesterday.

All The-Committee-For-Counting-The-Cats-Of-Calcutta is certain about is that there are going to be more cats in Calcutta tomorrow than there are today.

Nobody knows why it is that crows pursue hawks on the quais of Calcutta; while in every other port it is the hawks that pursue the crows.

All The-Committee-For-Counting-The-Hawks-Of-Calcutta is sure about is that, if the crows keep it up, there are going to be fewer hawks in Calcutta tomorrow than there are today.

Nobody knows how many cows there are in Calcutta. All The-Committee-For-Counting-The-Cows-Of-Calcutta is sure about is that some are standing up but others are lying down. It looks like the work of The-Committee-For-Counting-The-Cows-Of-Calcutta will have to be divided into a Committee-For-Cows-Standing-Up and a Committee-For-Counting-Cows-Lying-Down.

Nobody knows why the dogs of Calcutta never bark, but run away. All that The-Committee-For-Counting-The-Dogs-Of-Calcutta can report is that you have to catch a dog before you can count him—and how can you count him when he runs away?

At this writing it appears that there are going to be more people on The-Committee-For-Counting-People-In-Calcutta at this time tomorrow than there are today.

We plan to tackle that as soon as The-Committee-Dividing-The-Work-Of-The-Committee-For-Counting-Cows has been organized.

A bureaucrat of nine fell into step beside me, wearing only a pair of ragged shorts. His arms, thin as reeds, had been tattooed with a butterfly on one arm and a cobra on the other.

"Go to ship, Papa?" he wanted to know.

I nodded yes.

"You go wrong way to ship, Papa."

I was going the right way. But if I believed I was going wrong I would hire him to guide me, and he'd take me to the ship by another route. He took my hand. I took it away.

"You want to go to American movie, Papa?"

I didn't answer. He kept stepping right with me. I increased my pace. He increased his.

"You want to go to library, Papa?"

I made no answer. His hard little fingernails clawed my arm. I came to a dead stop.

He deadstopped too.

I made a feinting movement to the right.

He feinted to my right.

I feinted to the left. He feinted to my left.

I made a fast U-turn and hurried in the opposite direction. He hurried with me. I broke into a run. He ran with me. I stopped to get my breath. He stopped too.

"Don't you have a home?" I asked him.

He nodded. Yes. He had a home.

"Why don't you go there then?"

"Cannot go to home without *baksheesh,* Papa."

I offered him a dime. He shook his head. No.

"What's wrong with a dime?" I wanted to know.

"*Quarter,* Papa."

"Go to hell," I told him, and reversed my direction back toward the ship.

He stayed beside me. I broke into a run. I was six feet long and he was four, but he maintained the pace. I ran faster.

We ran along a wall. What was on the other side I had no idea—but it would only take a moment to scoop him up, toss him over and lose him forever. He seemed to divine some such intention; because he put himself out of reaching distance without losing stride.

I ducked, between hacks, across a street: he ducked between hacks with me. I raced back across the same street: he raced with me. Now I had only a few yards to go to a gate he could not enter.

I reached it and leaned against it, knees shaking, heart racing, chest heaving, sweat pouring. He wasn't even out of breath—merely stood there regarding me curiously.

"Eckersize, Papa?"

It *could* be put that way. It felt more like the wildest workout in town.

"*Baksheesh,* Papa?"

I handed him a cigar.

"Match, Papa?"

The *Malaysia Mail* loomed ominously at the quai. A line of porters were toting sacks of flour off her into a warehouse. Danielsen was leaning over the rail. He watched me climbing the ramp as if waiting to tell me something.

"I thought you were at Ezekiel's," I told him.

"Customs are questioning the old man," he explained, "they found a thousand watches behind Manning's medicine cabinet. He thought his medicine cabinet had immunity from inspection."

I started to feel elation; then my elation died.

"What do they want with the old man?"

"They want to know whether he was in on it."

"Do you think so?"

"No."

"How much could he have gotten for the loot?"

206

"At least thirty thousand."

"I'd never have given him credit for the nerve," I had to admit.

It came to me, at last, how strongly fear had been driving Manning.

In my stateroom I picked up an accusation of Hemingway, yellow with years, written by a critic named Rascoe, now forgotten, in the thirties. Hemingway was infantile when he had written *The Sun Also Rises* and had since grown increasingly childish, Rascoe had decided. On the other hand, James T. Farrell had reached the full flowering of his maturity. Well, good.

I found another review, of a decade later, entitled "The Dark Night of Ernest Hemingway," which proclaimed Hemingway's failure "because there is no freedom in work when it becomes compulsion. The word for that is anarchy—a strange God to put before God. Personally, I would settle for just one story in which the Ten Commandments did not get kicked all over the place." When Billy Graham came along Hemingway lost *this* critic for certain.

If Hemingway hadn't written himself out in the twenties, as Rascoe had announced, he'd certainly written himself out in the thirties—left-wing critics were agreed by the forties: the writer to watch, however, was no longer Farrell. Now it was Howard Fast.

Somehow or other Hemingway *must* have managed to keep writing through the forties, because, by the fifties, it was clearly understood that now he had *really* written himself out. There was always somebody else who was more mature, someone more profound; someone more promising. Someone more true.

Yet the forties had passed, and the fifties had passed, and new critics came on and old critics passed; and new writers came on, and old writers failed and still Hemingway stood them off. Like Sal Maglie, he had nothing left and yet he won ball games. And still he went to the wars and still he went to the bullfights and still he enjoyed his life against all the rules: until he had not only the full pack of American Podhoretzes in pursuit, but European Podhoretzes as well.

"I do not like that old man," one boy, withered by bitterness, because others were richer, wrote for *L'Express,* "for certain reasons I have simmered all along in the reading of his books. This man is a comedian who during all his life walked around with his testicles for a necklace. But I do suspect that he has none, and that he is a comedian whose literature, by means of tricks, realizes nothing more than the assumptions of *Reader's Digest.* Ernesto's virility is wine and literature. Don Ernesto is afflicted with an awfully sly and wicked look. Hiding behind his beard, Don Ernesto has a mischievous air, mischievous, *very* mischievous."

I remembered this withered boy. He'd once petitioned Jean-Paul Sartre for employment as a secretary, but had later to be dismissed for selling old manuscripts of Sartre's on the sly. The game worked so long as buyers were interested only in collecting—when one began publishing, somebody had to go. He went. Apparently in pursuit of Hemingway. Some people can't wait to get rich.

"In nearly all of Hemingway's books we feel his sympathy with those who are worthy of it," one faint-praiser observed; failing to realize that the great thing about the man's books is their sympathy for those unworthy of it.

"There are no *women* in his books!" Professor Fiedler exclaims. "If in *For Whom the Bell Tolls* Hemingway has written the most absurd love-scene in the history of the American novel it is not because he lost momentarily his skill and authority. It is a giveaway—a moment which illuminates the whole erotic content of his fiction."

Catch that "if." Because when the Professor himself revealed a homosexual relationship between Huck Finn and Nigger Jim, he extended absurdity in love scenes into naked asininity. Thereby illuminating nothing but the Professor.

Well, there's one on every campus. In Fiedler we have the classic mediocrity avenging itself for its deprivation. His method is the equivalent process, in academic terms, of Hollywood writers in "licking a book into shape."

Fiedler employs symbolism to drain art of its life. He does not criticize: he adapts. By transferring the writer's meaning into arbitrary abstractions, he can leave any work for dead.

We find, for example, that Hemingway's description of Mount Kilimanjaro, in *The Short Happy Life of Francis MacComber,* as "wide as all the world, great, high and unbelievably white" *really* means (says the Professor) "the whiteness from which the American author tries so vainly to flee, the bland whiteness of the irrational taboo in Melville, and antarctic whiteness of polar disaster in Poe, the whiteness of the White Goddess herself—who having been denied as giver of life and source of love, must be recognized as dealer of death!"

All he overlooked is that Hemingway wasn't talking of anything but snow. All the rest of the stuff is simply the Professor earning a living. Talentlessness, like asexuality, is never passive, but finds another outlet.

The Professor's trouble is simply that he himself cannot react to womanhood unless it is wrapped in erudition enfolded in a symbol tied by a ribbon made of concepts. What he demands is one of those Puritan euphemisms about "the mystery of femininity." Hemingway disposed of the mystery and presented a woman.

"What Hemingway's emphasis on the ritual murder of fish conceals," the Professor continues, "that it is not so much the sport as the occasion for immersion which is essential to the holy marriage of males. Water is the symbol of the barrier between the Great Good Place and the busy world of women."

He boasts of wounds who never bore a scar: he disbelieves that the earth can move who has never felt it move.

What is saddening about this piggish jargon is that young people with a love of literature pay for courses to learn how to speak it.

I was glad to be interrupted by a knock. It was Danielsen.

"Manning bought the watches in Kowloon," Danielsen told me, "the merchant tipped off the Customs police. They make a good raid now and then to cover bribery. This was their good one."

"What happens with Manning?"

"If the company stands by him with an American lawyer he'll get the case transferred to the States. If the company fires him he might have to do time here—I wouldn't wish that on the worst dog that ever lived."

"Can't he get his own lawyer?"

"Manning doesn't have a nickel. In debt. Alimony. More fouled up than Crooked-Neck."

"I have to get back into town," I told Danielsen, "are you coming?"

"I'll see you at Ezekiel's," he told me.

"The hell you will," I thought.

Chips, wearing a Hawaiian shirt, was lounging outside the door of the stateroom in which Manning was under arrest.

210

"I want to see *him* getting *his,*" he told me, "*with* the manacles."

He crossed his wrists to be sure I understood what manacles were.

"When am I getting mine?" I wanted to know.

"When I get a draw," he promised me again.

The quai was full of old shadows. Out of one came a nine-year-old bureaucrat.

"Hello, Papa."

He was smoking a cigar. "I paid you to go home," I reminded him, "no more *baksheesh.*"

He skipped along as confidently as before.

"Cigar, Papa?"

When I got through the gate I jumped into a cab and slammed the door on him hard.

"Kanani Mansions," I told the driver.

Kanani Mansions

Black-market rascals came and went, sedate Sikhs moved Sikhishly about their Sikhish business; American seamen rapped all the wrong doors and *ayahs* skittered like withered leaves down the careworn corridors of Kanani Mansions.

The whores of Calcutta don't live like the whores of Bombay. In that bootlegging, Puritanical, black-marketing, dreadful Bombay, there are no bars for a seaman to find a wife for a week or a month. There are only the great cat-houses (more like curtained cow-houses) run on short-term love. These; and the animalized women of the cages of Kamathipura.

But in Calcutta's flashing bars, thronging with attractive girls from every port of Asia, a seaman can find long-term love. This circumstance makes it possible for such a woman as Martha to keep an apartment of her own with civilized appointments: Martha had a high bookshelf lined with books and records—mostly American—as well as her own bedroom, bath, kitchen and a small parlor. She supported an *ayah,* an infant son and her mother.

Martha's mother, Anna, did not live with her. Although Martha's trade was of her mother's devising, and Anna would have preferred to live with her daughter, Martha kept her at a distance in a small apartment down the hall.

A certain looseness in her look and a cleverness in her eyes distinguished mother from daughter more than her years. Anna's coldly whorish air left Martha seeming to be the more motherly woman of the two.

Martha was darker. Anna hennaed her hair and powdered her face too heavily; to make herself look less Asiatic. Every afternoon she came in dressed for a ball, with a copy of the trial of one Commander Nanavati, a naval officer who had shot and killed his wife's lover.

She would insist on reading excerpts of the trial to us whether we would or no.

Martha's little *ayah* ran for cover as soon as Anna came in. These homeless old women who serve as maids-of-all-work in return for a corner of a floor to sleep on and the leftovers of a table to subsist on, can be obtained anywhere in Calcutta simply by going down the street and finding one, already starving, on the curb.

"Get rid of that one," Anna would command Martha, "she'll steal the carpet while you're asleep."

"She is honest," Martha defended the old dry leaf huddled, listening, behind a chair.

This *ayah,* whose past had no meaning, whose future no one cared about, knew that Anna was speaking of her unfavorably.

"Send her back to the street," Anna urged.

"She is good with the boy," Martha replied.

So many autumns had blown down from the north, since this wisp out of the hills of Assam had first come begging into the heat of Calcutta, that they were now beyond counting. Yet the old cracked brown grandmother had a life of her own along the floor; that she shared with Martha's infant son.

While Martha and I and Anna lived among records, shelves, chairs and windows, the infant boy and the very old woman crept in and out of caves made of pillows; or hid together under the divan.

Music, the sound of voices, arguments, orders, food and tea all came down to them mysteriously from somewhere above. And although the *ayah* did not understand what was being said when we spoke in English, she sensed enough to stay in hiding while Anna carried on about this "fair-looking person of thirty-seven and Commander of I.N.S. *Mysore,* who was accused in the murder case of PREM BHAGWANDAS AHUJA, an automobile dealer."

Martha retired to the bedroom when Anna began reading.

Even The-Ayah-Who-Lived-On-The-Floor stopped crawling about when Anna got into the heart of the matter of Commander Nanavati.

But after a while Anna herself would grow bored with this endless Nanavati. Then she'd go for the Scotch.

The Scotch was *The Best Procurable,* the same brand that Hemingway had once offered me. A Hollywood producer, I remembered, also used to keep a bottle of the same handy— but *he* wouldn't open it.

"You are of New York?" Anna wanted to know while she was pouring. "Do you want ice?"

"Yes. I mean no. I mean yes, I want ice, but I am not of New York. I am of Chicago."

"Is that far from Los Angeles?"

"As far as the width of India," I answered; with no clearer notion of India's width than she had of Chicago.

"I understand you have written a biography of Frank Sinatra," Anna told me. "He *must* be a *wonderful* person."

"A *great* human being," I assured the poor creature—why disenchant her?

"*All* that money," she marveled, a dream all of glass spinning behind her eyes—"he must spend a great deal on women."

215

"He gives most of it to charity," I decided. As long as I was Frankie's biographer I might as well be on his side.

"He must give wonderful parties," the woman dreamed on, "in Colorful Los Angeles."

"The last one wasn't in Los Angeles," I seemed to recall, "he threw it in the cove below Niagara Falls."

Anna clasped her hands—"What *that* must have cost!"

"A pretty penny," I guessed, "but the man has such marvelous luck he *always* ends up ahead. Somebody started a dice game when the guests started to leave, and Frank won more than enough to pay for renting the cove. I lost everything I had," I added defensively.

"I'm sorry," she told me.

"Small matter," I assured her, "it's easy come easy go in Colorful Los Angeles."

My mind returned to that bottle of *The Best Procurable* that I couldn't get the producer to open in Los Angeles. That city of Good Procurers.

There I'd lived in an encrusted crypt entitled The Garden of Allah Chateau—which ought to indicate how far ahead of the rest of the world L.A. was. It was already orbiting in 1950.

Most of the residents of The Chateau were independents— actors, writers and producers; and several were not only independent as artists but independent of the entire human race. The Chateau at sunset, in fact, looked like a reunion of the garden party Alice's Wicked Queen once gave. There were several wicked queens on the premises and a few wicked kings as well.

The Wickedest of any was the Wicked Producer. I knew he was wicked because he toted this huge bottle about, tucked resolutely under his arm as if firmly determined to get everybody drunk. I saw immediately I would have to be careful.

I knew he was a producer because he wore sunglasses tinted

216

chartreuse and open-toed sandals whose protruding toes were tinted a matching shade.

His name was Schlepker. Otto Schlepker.

It wouldn't be fair to call Otto grasping as he often let me hold his bottle for minutes at a time. *"Read that label,"* he would say, and, after a moment—"Read it out *loudt.*"

"The Best Scotch Procurable," I would read aloud, looking at him appealingly.

"Let me be open with you," he offered, taking the bottle back and looking hooded, "you have noticed I am not a happy man?"

"Well, I didn't think of you as being downright happy so much as just gruesomely smug," I had had to confess.

"I *force* myself to look contented," Otto confessed, "actually, I am a tragic person. All my life I have thoughtlessly devoted my life to selfish interests and now I am paying the price—I have pangs of guilt so secret only my analyst knows where to find them. But unless I begin doing things for other people right away the secret pangs will destroy me. As I have already spent over three thousand dollars on my analyst I cannot afford doubt. That would be throwing money away. I'm going to start living for others if it kills me. I will make a movie that will show the terrible suffering of drug addicts that will make a million dollars."

A human soul stood before me naked and imperiled. I would give him succor in his spiritual struggle. Nothing short of that was going to get him to open that bottle.

I ought to explain that I was in California on a Hollywood Fulbright. That is the kind whereby a studio will allot five hundred dollars to an independent producer toward the entertainment of an out-of-town writer upon the assumption that a week's free feeding will so fill the recipient with gratitude that he will sign anything just to show he is a good old sport.

When the word got around that a studio was picking up my tabs at Romanoff's, a marvelous change came over the occupants of the Chateau. Where they had heretofore appeared indifferent to my career, they now began competing good-naturedly with one another to give me friendly advice. When my allotment ran out we were blocking traffic.

With the allotment run out and still no signature, there was a danger that the Wicked Independent Producer would find himself merely Independently Wicked. He did not wish to threaten me, he threatened me, but unless I signed he would blacken my name with everyone in Schwartz's drugstore.

"Whatever am I to do in this crisis?"—I turned to my agent who was dealing himself a solitaire hand with mutuel tickets. "I am depending on your wisdom, acquired by long years of toiling in the vineyards of Art."

"Jump ship and pan for gold," the agent advised me, and won the hand.

At that moment the large producer materialized, accompanied by a small gimp.

"I want you to meet a Dedicated Fan," the producer introduced him.

"To whom, sir," I inquired courteously, "are you dedicated?"

"Why," he told me, "to *you*. May I see some identification?"

"You want me to *identify* myself?" I asked.

"I can't risk dedicating myself to an impostor," the friendly fellow explained.

I showed him my library card and my army serial number. These distinctions satisfied him. For he handed me a packet

218

of attractively colored papers and left looking even more dedicated.

As any process server ought when leaving a client properly subpoenaed. So this was Hollywood.

Otto handed me the bottle of the best procurable as if to apologize for threatening me with the law. It was the first time I'd been invited to a party and ordered to jail by the same man with a single gesture. I didn't know how to react to Otto. This may have been because Otto didn't know how to react to himself.

He turned on his heel in a lurching safari with myself lurching solemnly after him, my benefactor; clutching my subpoenas and my Scotch to my breast with equal ardor.

He did a hard right and braked. I almost ran the man down. He drew himself up and, literally striking his own breast, declaimed, "I'm a *nice* fellow! I do *good* for everybody! *Why do you make me act so damned cheap?*"

Transfixed by the realization of what I was doing to a fellow human being, my guilt was self-proclaiming.

"Open the Scotch!" he roared at me. *"Or isn't the best procurable good enough for you?"* And handed me the contract he'd been begging me to sign.

"It is surely the *very* best procurable," I confessed meekly, hurrying to put my signature down while he still permitted me to make such a small atonement, "so it will have to do until we can get a bottle of the best that is unprocurable," I added hopefully.

Martha came out of the bedroom dressed to go out.

Anna picked up *Commander on Trial,* determined to resume the story of Nanavati's trial. But a low growl from the corner where the *ayah* hid, protested. Every time Anna began to read, the *ayah* growled.

"She is stealing the brandy," Anna warned Martha, "I smelled it on her when I came in."

How a person so soaked in *The Best Procurable* could tell what anyone else had been drinking was something I couldn't figure.

"I want you to leave," Martha told Anna.

Even the *ayah* was glad to see her go.

Martha seemed contented, most of the day, to lounge about in Indian robes, idling the hours between her record player and her son.

She had been married, at sixteen, to a man of Shillong; who had deserted her shortly after their son had been born. She'd had one letter from him, postmarked London; that had contained neither money nor a promise of it. It had sounded as though he had remarried.

The photograph on her bookshelf was of a middle-aged American wearing a maritime officer's cap. It was signed: *With all my love to Martha—Jeff.*

When she'd put on her Western clothes we'd wheel about Calcutta for an hour.

We both looked forward to that late afternoon hour when the sun softened the city's ancestral walls to amber. Then we rode into the first flares of the night past trees like clouds at rest. We'd have dinner at a restaurant as far from Ezekiel's as I could take her; and buy her roses—one rupee per bunch—before we had to go back.

Her father had been a physician of Shillong. Anna had spent a great deal of money entertaining men younger than herself. The physician had at last divorced her and remarried, severing all connection with his first family.

Anna had then pressed Martha to leave Shillong and come to Calcutta until Martha had given in.

Anna had brought an American home with her.

He was a seaman of twenty and had been displeased with the older woman. Anna had taken money that belonged to him while they had been drinking.

"A man who wants to make love to *me,* must pay," Anna had justified herself in taking the boy's money.

"I don't want to make love to you, old dog," the seaman had answered.

"Now you insult me, you cannot have your money back," Anna had decided.

"Give the man his money, Anna," Martha had instructed her mother.

"He gets nothing," Anna had been stubborn.

"I ought to whip you," the seaman had threatened her.

"You want to beat somebody?" Anna had picked up the threat—"beat *her*—she's the one you want to make love to, *isn't* she?"

The sailor had not denied it. It was Martha or his money back. Anna wouldn't give up the money.

Martha had taken him into the bedroom.

"I gave you life," Anna reproached her after the seaman had left, "now you take away my sweethearts."

"I do not like to sell my bud-*dee,*" Martha would say at the same hour every night. As if, just by saying it, she could delay the night at Ezekiel's.

She was disliked by Ezekiel's other B-girls: they mistook her contempt for this trade as contempt for themselves, and her beauty sharpened their resentment.

Yet she was not truly a beauty. The bridge of her nose was a bit too broad, and she lacked perhaps half an inch of being of average height. Yet her face was abundant with warmth and light.

"They are all like Anna," she told me of the other women of Ezekiel's—"they think I take their sweethearts."

221

I knew she didn't need to take their sweethearts. Seaman and tourist alike were drawn toward her, and not merely for her looks. This woman had such inner calm that her presence lent others a sense of repose.

One night, after she had come in late and had fallen asleep immediately, I wakened, later, to feel her arms come around me. Yet it wasn't lovemaking on her mind. She needed to talk.

"I do not like to sell my bud-*dee*," she wanted me to understand, "because if I do this, how am I to belong to the child?"

"Don't you feel you belong to him now?"

"I belonged to him in Shillong. I belonged, also, to my father. I belonged, then, to Shillong. Now I belong to nothing. And I cannot go back to Shillong. I thought I belonged to Jeff, but then Jeff go. I think maybe I belong to you; but soon you go. How can I belong to the child when I do not belong to myself? I belong to Ezekiel's, nothing more." She began to cry softly.

I did not try to console her.

*

I hadn't been aboard the *Malaysia Mail*, nor seen any of the crew, for over a week. I'd avoided going into Ezekiel's, when I dropped Martha off there, and waited for her at home.

I got along well with the Ayah-Who-Lived-On-The-Floor by means of such small gifts as the butts of cigars or a nip of brandy. It was like spending the evening with a small, intelligent, domesticated monkey. Sometimes, without a word, she would bring me tea.

I would feel a touch on my knee and she would be crouched, holding the cup and saucer out to me and grinning from ear to ear. The old woman had beautiful teeth.

When Martha and I took a cab in the evening, I would have the driver stop by the quai, just to make sure that the ship was still in port. There would always be a great crane unloading cargo off the deck, and a line of porters carrying fresh cargo into the hold. I had no idea either of what was being unloaded or of what was being taken on. Sometimes I caught glimpses of Sparks or Chips or Danielsen or Bridelove or Muncie. I didn't see Manning. Sufficient unto the day, I thought.

"What kind place is Shy-Ann?" Martha asked me on one of these evening spins. "What kind place in America?"

"Shy-Ann?"

"Shy-Ann in Why-O-Ming."

"Oh. Wyoming is in the West of America."

"Why people of Why-O-Ming call me monkey?"

"Why should people call you monkey?"

Martha touched a finger to her cheek: "Dark."

She was brooding about her American engineer. Whoever he was, he was a kuke; he had bewildered this girl.

His letters, that she'd asked me to read, were dense with endearments and plans for bringing her to Cheyenne.

"I wait many day," she remembered now. "Jeff come at last. Him very good to me and boy. I not have to sell my bud-*dee*. Then, middle of night, big knock on door. I turn on light. Jeff not in bed. Jeff *outside* door making big noise. 'Whore!' he speak at me—'Whore! Open door!' *What* I gonna do? I not open, police come. I open. He hit. Keep hitting. I fall. He kick. Jeff *dronk*."

Now the letters of endearment had begun again; filled with the same old plans. The desperation of her situation was tempting Martha to believe that, if she gave Jeff a second chance, he might mean it after all and take her to America. Whatever might happen to her in Cheyenne could hardly be worse, she felt, than what was happening to her in Calcutta.

"You think this man *love?*" she asked me.

223

"He love alright," I assured her, "for sure."

"Then why he *hit?*"

"Because to be in love makes a man no longer free, and not to be free makes him angry. He would rather give you money and go away."

"In Why-O-Ming, will I have to sell my bud-*dee?*"

"As the wife of an American engineer making eight hundred dollars a month I shouldn't think so," I told her; but the way things are changing I couldn't be sure.

Jeff, I felt, had problems.

One was the hard time he was going to have convincing his neighbors in Cheyenne that his wife wasn't a squaw.

The other was tougher, being within himself. My hunch was that Jeff was a churchgoing, college- educated middle-class man who believed in being sorry for whores and kind to Indians—but to fall in love with an Indian whore! Wouldn't that be degrading himself? The man was in the switches without a doubt. If he weren't he'd come and get her and take her home and be damned to the neighbors; instead he was turning destructive.

The cab wheeled us to Ezekiel's. I never hung around Ezekiel's long after I'd taken Martha there, and she didn't want me standing by. If I saw anyone there from the ship I'd have a drink with him, then get out. Danielsen, sitting by himself as he always sat, looked like he was waiting for somebody.

"Your girl friend have a friend?" he asked me.

"She lives by herself," I explained, "what's the matter with the stuff walking around?"

"I don't go for the short-term deal," he explained. "I'm not like Sparks, a new thing every night. I want the same thing. We may be here another week."

"Don't look now," I changed the subject, "but did you notice what just came in with a jug in his hand?"

It had to be Crooked-Neck, his head slowly revolving; and carrying a gin-fifth simply by a finger thrust into it for a stopper. By that continuous slow rotation both Danielsen and myself had the apprehension that Smith was getting in shape to surpass himself in fouling himself up as well as everybody within fouling-up distance.

"Hi-*ee*," he greeted us with one hand on Danielsen's shoulder and his bottle-hand on my own, "shall we bound a bit on the waves, my boys? Shall we zig? Shall we zag? What course shall we steer?"

"I'm thinking seriously of getting laid," Danielsen announced like a Papal Edict.

I wanted to shake off Smith.

"Kanani Mansions is *swarming*," I suggested.

"Let's go," Danielsen said quickly. He wanted to shake Smith too.

"See you on the ship, sailor," I told Smith, to make our departure final.

Danielsen wouldn't ride an Indian taxi unless it were driven by a Sikh. We found one that was satisfactory because the Sikh had a white beard.

"Smith," Danielsen advised me in the cab, "is dangerous."

"So I've been told," I answered.

Although Anna must have been a couple of years older than Danielsen, she appeared ten years younger. Fairer than Martha, with an oval face where Martha's was square-jawed, her hair dyed red and worn in bangs—befitting the green that flecked her eyes whenever she thought about money—she made a strong impression upon him. When she led him to a pink settee and began brushing his colorless hair with her hand, she cinched that impression. A pink blush rose to Danielsen's cheeks that matched the settee's strange hue. He was in good hands.

I was fixing the drinks when the knock came.

Crooked-Neck stood in the open door, still gently revolving his ominous skull, his bottle still attached to the finger.

I'd said "Kanani Mansions" too loudly.

Yet Anna welcomed him warmly. An American was an American regardless of the angle at which his head might be attached was her thinking. When she went into her small kitchen, I followed.

"Sick," I whispered in her ear, spinning a finger at my temple and indicating her new guest, "a Crazy."

"All Americans are Crazies," Anna told me. "You are a Crazy too."

Smith declined the drink she offered, preferring to unstop his own bottle, wash gin between his cheeks for a minute, then swallow it down with great boggling jumps of his Adam's apple.

Danielsen's set of the blues began darkening. He never held a fleeting doubt that *anyone,* who wanted to take the trouble to do so, could take *any* woman he wished away from Danielsen.

"I was batting the breeze with this Anglo chick in a bar on Ho-Phang Road," Smith began relating cheerfully, "and it got toward closing time. She told me if I wanted to spend fifteen dollars I could come up to her place and stay all night. I said I'd like that only all I had was thirteen. She said 'That'll do.'

" 'But I have to get out early,' I told her, 'to get back to my ship.' She said, 'That's alright, I'll set the alarm.' I said, 'Well, alright, but I'll need cab-fare to get back.' She said, 'I'll see you get back alright.' 'I feel awfully crummy,' I said, and she said 'I'll draw you a bath.' 'This shirt is like a rag,'

226

I told her. 'There's a couple of new shirts at my place you can have,' she told me. I said, 'Gee, Honey, that's swell, but we can't go up there and just *look* at one another.' So she said, 'We'll pick up a couple of bottles on the way.' So we got a cab and picked up a couple of bottles and went to her place and she cooked up ham and eggs. There was a suit of my size hanging in the clothes-closet. She says would I like to see her dance with nothing on but her shoes and stockings, so I said, 'Gee, Honey, that would be great.' So she mixed the drinks and turned on the record player and danced naked holding her hand between her legs. Wonderful figure. After a while we went to bed. I could still kick myself when I think about it."

"What are you kicking yourself about?" I obliged Smith— "It sounds like you got a pretty fair shake."

"I wanted to see if she made good on her promises," he explained, "but she didn't."

"What happened?" I asked.

"I forgot the suit in the closet," Smith explained, "and she forgot to remind me."

"Why didn't you go back and pick it up?" I asked.

"I didn't have the time. I phoned her. I asked her to bring it down to the dock."

"Did she?"

Smith looked at me cynically. "Did you ever know a broad to keep her word?"

"Why should any woman keep her word to anyone like you," I heard Danielsen asking quite distinctly, "no woman in her right mind could respect you."

Anna stopped stirring the ice in her glass and looked over at me curiously. I looked out the window at the roofs of Calcutta. I hoped Smith would have the sense to let it pass.

He did. "You're kidding," was all he said, and laughed un-

227

easily; knowing Danielsen wasn't kidding at all. I forced myself to glance at Danielsen.

He looked positively gaunt. And the shadow of an old determination lent his face an expression too fixed. Yet he'd had only two drinks.

Anna rose, put a record on, and went to Danielsen with her hands outstretched.

He didn't take them.

"Dance with your boy friend," he ordered her.

"I don't even know the woman, Danielsen," Smith said, trying to sound casual.

Anna wore a sheepish look, like anyone who doesn't know her next move.

"I told you to *dance* with him," Danielsen let her know what her best move was. "I *told* you. And I'm getting pretty well fed-up waiting."

"I'll dance with her if you want me to, Danielsen," Smith offered amiably, and added, as he ought *not* to have added, with the pair dancing stiffly under Danielsen's eye—"I just don't see what you're getting so cocky about."

Danielsen put down his glass too carefully.

"Turn off that record," he commanded me. I turned it off.

"I'll *tell* you what I'm getting cocky about, sailor," Danielsen told him, "you're a clap-ridden forty-year-old degenerate running a crooked card game, *that's* what I'm getting cocky about."

Smith sat down across the room. He wasn't going to precipitate a fight. But he was going to draw a real firm line.

"Alright," he told Danielsen. "I *do* have the clap. Since *you* say so, I'm a degenerate. And I *do* run a crooked card game. But I'm *not* forty. I'm only thirty-nine. And that makes you out a liar."

228

Danielsen swung into the kitchen and swung back with a bread knife. We were in business.

Smith stood up, looking toward me yet watching Danielsen. Anna waited dead-white under her rouge.

I got a chair in front of me.

Danielsen looked ridiculous, but he was holding the knife right. He began tiptoeing, then sprang—Smith leaped clean over the pink settee, tilted it in front of him, holding it by its springs, with his back to the wall: as perfect a fort as I've ever seen constructed in two seconds. There was absolutely no way of Danielsen getting at him.

Danielsen's eyes, glazing around the room to find where Smith had gone, skipped across Anna and found me. It was *my* move.

All I had was the chair behind which I was standing.

Smith put his nose over the top of the red settee.

"Don't throw the chair," he advised me conversationally; and pulled his nose back.

The settee moved an inch toward Danielsen; Danielsen didn't see it move. Smith was holding it, a bit off the ground, by its springs. Even at that moment I realized how much strength that required.

Danielsen began trying to ask me something. I could tell only because his lips were moving.

"I can't hear you, Danielsen," I told him with my hands on the chair's back. He raised his voice.

"The last stitch," he told me—"you're asking for it."

I shifted my eyes. He followed the shift, saw the settee coming and came at me blade first as Smith lunged with the settee—and missed. I thrust the chair upward to block the blade. It went into the chair's rattan bottom and stuck.

Smith lay sprawling. I leaped across him and got to the

door while Danielsen was extricating the knife. As I opened the door he turned and leaped across Smith.

It was me he wanted.

I knew I was running only because two long dark walls, on either side, kept passing me. I knew I'd fallen because the walls weren't moving. I rolled over onto my back just in time to get both hands on the wrist that held the knife.

Danielsen was astride me with the blade four inches off my heart.

I held.

I was the strongest man in the world. I held it and cried up to the blind eyes looking down:

"Danielsen! Danielsen!"

Through a dark and distant land he heard his name called once—and called again.

The blindness faded from his eyes.

But not the rage.

Now he knew who he was. He *knew* who I was. He saw the knife. And knew he could kill me.

And he didn't know why he shouldn't.

He switched the knife to his free hand.

There was nothing I could do. The decision was Danielsen's.

"You asked for it. You *want* it now?"

"No," I assured him, without knowing what *it* was, "I *don't* want it."

Then he smiled that ever-so-wan, ever-so-lonesome, terrible smile.

"You've got me," I assured him. "You win."

"Get up," he commanded me.

I got up.

"Run for your life."

I ran. For my life.

230

I ran for Anna's door. I shut the door and locked it. I turned.

Smith had Anna spread-legged on the naked springs, her dress over her head, screwing like a madman.

I went into the kitchen and found whiskey and a cup. I had to hold the cup with both hands to bring it to my lips. Then I had another. My shakiness diminished to an interior quivering: I was going to quiver inwardly for some time to come, I realized.

When I came out of the kitchen Anna was huddled on the floor, her dress ripped down the middle. Smith was sitting on the edge of the settee buttoning his pants.

A high shrill shout challenged us from the other side of the door.

"Anyone *one* of us! Last stitch! Last stitch!"

"Go back to the ship, Danielsen," I called.

"Last stitch through your nose!"

Then his step fled lightly down the hall.

Anna had recovered sufficiently to sit up, holding her dress together while shifting her dazed look between us: she didn't know which one of us had raped her.

"Don't leave me with him," she decided, looking at me.

The night's events were just a series of cheerful little coincidences to Smith, but they'd left me exhausted; the only thing that kept me from leaving was the fear that Danielsen might be waiting in the hall. I waited until Smith was ready to leave too.

He was taking his ease by cracking peanuts between his palms and spitting the shells out onto the carpet.

"After you get through picking up the shells, sailor," I suggested, "we'll set the settee rightside up."

Smith studied me thoughtfully.

"For a man whose life I've just saved you don't sound

overly grateful," he reproached me. And spat another shell onto the carpet.

"Don't leave me alone with him," Anna repeated.

But I waited at one end of the settee until Smith felt sufficiently obliging to get his can off of it long enough for me to upend it. Then he sat down again.

"Didn't you know that Danielsen is beach-nuts?" he asked me.

"I know now," I told Smith, tossing him his cap.

"What do you think you'd have if you put Danielsen's brain in a cat?" Smith wanted to know. "That's a riddle, son," he explained, grinning contentedly. He'd enjoyed every minute of the row, it was plain.

"Don't leave me alone with him," Anna said again.

"She don't want to be left alone with you," Smith told me. "What do you think you'd have? *Guess.*"

"Why don't you *both* go?" the woman asked weakly.

Smith jammed a finger into his bottle and got up.

"Coming, Pops?" he asked at the door.

"I'm coming."

"Just want me to wait out first, eh?" he asked, grinning.

"You're cutting in close," I admitted, "after you."

There was no shadow, in that long hall, of Danielsen.

"What's the next stop, Pops?" he asked me, more ready than ever for anything.

My own next step was bed and that bed wasn't far. But I waited till I had the key in the lock before I let Smith know how close to home I was.

"See you on the ship, sailor," I told him; let myself in and barred the door behind me.

If Danielsen was waiting down the hall, Crooked-Neck Smith had a problem. It no longer interested me.

"Wait till Anna gets Martha's ear tomorrow," I thought.

Martha's boy was curled up on the couch.

I helped myself to the brandy on the bookshelf.

There was a knock on the door.

"What do you want?" I called through the door.

"What you'd have *is a crazy cat!*" Smith whooped—and I heard him walking off laughing his head off all the way.

I lit a cigar and began reading *Commander on Trial:*

A car running at a stormy speed on the Flora Fountain Road turned suddenly towards a magnificent building in the beautiful city of BOMBAY, knows as "JEEVAN JYOT." The gate of the Car was opened with a zerking sound and a hand-some man of dominating personality exactly six feet tall came out, pushing the door back and rushed straight towards the upper stairs, a place well known to him.

It was a hot afternoon of April 27, 1959. People were gasping for wind. Pitch on the road was melting, the sea was calm, which was the clear indication of some unexpected storm.

BANG...! BANG...!! BANG...!!! was the sound which naturally diverted the attention of the passers-by. This unusual gun shot in a residential flat made people curious to know about the reasons for this unfortunate event. Before the persons assembled outside could know the reason they saw the dramatic turn of an Officer looking man, running down with a naked revolver in his hand. Automatically, it created a curiosity among people assembled outside the gate to know what actually had happened. The well dressed man wearing a spotless Fawn colored shirt and a pair of dark colored trousers appeared. From his very appearance it looked as if his excellent character was blotted with some undesirable act, which was clearly reflected from

233

his perplexed appearance. The Durwan of the building tried to stop him but he could not.

POLICE! POLICE!! cried the mob, but the man did not care for police, got into the Car and without properly answering the queries of DURWAN and others, he went on, though he uttered some thing but exactly he could not remember as his conscience was guilty.

Taking a sharp turn he drove fast assuring the people outside, in hurry and went to a Police Constable on duty. He slowed down his car. It was Government House Lower Gate where he stopped for a while and asked the Constable, who was on fixed post duty, the nearest Police Station?

I looked up, feeling I was being watched. There was only an infant sleeping. I resumed reading:

"Will you take me to the Police Station" asked the man. "No, I am on fixed post duty and cannot move from here" told the Constable.

After enquiring of the Police Station and being told that the nearest Police Station was GAMDEVI P.S. he drove away. Now the man was totally undecided and was in half haphazard state of mind, completely perplexed and could not ascertain his further steps. He was under the impression as some thing unpleasant had happened. He had never imagined the consequences which actually happened because only an hour and a half before he was the man who was seen at METRO CINEMA dropping his beautiful blue eyed English born wife and his three kids. What a tragedy it was? That the wife was enjoying a film show on the screen and husband was playing a prominent role in another practical life drama outside the auditorium which was even more powerful and packed with thrills and fol-

234

lowed by unexpected events. How for a fate can play with a man no body can guess?

It was Commander Samuel's Office, where Commander in his white official dress was busy with his office routine. Suddenly he was diverted from his official work to an unofficial one, when another officer of same rank stepped in the office. He was well acquainted with him.

"I do not know exactly but I think I killed a man" said the man and asked his advice in this matter where the matter of accident according to his own belief was to be reported. The fact that the Smith & Mason .38 Service Revolver was used in this unfortunate event created an anxiety in Samuel's mind but he advised him the proper way and asked him to see Deputy Commissioner LOBO a C.I.D. Officer.

Actually this was an extraordinary event which happened for the first time in Commander's pleasant life.

"She is not faithful to me! She is not faithful to me"! ! were the repeated words which were rotating in his mind and even the whole picture of past was coming by and by to his mind, which he could not avoid. Thinking it better to submit himself to Police, he did so and relied upon the theory of accident and struggle.

The accused in this case, Commander Kavas Maneckshaw Nanavati a handsome well built man of 37, was a man of three battle fronts and had spent eighteen and a half years of his life in the Navy Service.

I glanced about the room and saw nobody but the sleeping infant. I got up and looked into the bedroom. Nobody. Then the bath. Nobody. The windows were secure. Danielsen had

frightened me more than I cared to admit to myself, I began
to think, when I saw her.

She was squatting like a watchful fox in a corner, that old
ayah who lived on the floor. And what had gotten her nose up
was my cigar.

I held it out to her and she came a-scuttering, snatched it
out of my hand, puffed at it twice while squatting, thrust it
back to my hand and, holding in the smoke she had inhaled,
held it until she'd scuttered back to her corner: there, her
eyes bright with pleasure, she let the smoke out. I'd never
seen anyone so old take so much joy out of so small a pleasure.

I returned to reading:

*Nanavati married Sylvia in England in 1949. The couple
had three children, the youngest being of three years. They
came to stay in a flat at Coloba in Bombay in December,
1957, as a Naval Officer Nanavati had to be away from
home for long periods of duty at sea. During 1958, Nanavati
was away from Bombay for about six months.*

*Mr. Trivedi said that Nanavati was introduced to Ahuja
by another naval officer, Lt. Cdr. Yagnik, in July or August,
1950. During the absence of Nanavati at Sea, his wife used
to visit Ahuja's house to see his sister, Miss Mammie Ahuja.
She also happened to meet Ahuja during those visits. Actually, Nanavati visited Ahuja's house along with his wife
only twice or thrice.*

*During these visits, the Prosecution said, "some intimacy
appears to have developed between Ahuja and Sylvia." On
April 18, 1959 Nanavati returned to Bombay. He took ten
days' leave from April 19 and stayed in Bombay. It was
during this leave period that the murder of Ahuja was
committed.*

The prosecutor told the jury that just before the return of Nanavati, Sylvia, it appeared, had written "some sort of a letter" to Ahuja. During the leave period Nanavati noticed a "sort of inexplicable coldness" on the part of Sylvia towards him. He was unhappy about this change in her attitude, but could not find out the exact reason.

On the morning of April 27, 1959 the date of the offence —the couple got up early and took their sick dog to a veterinary surgeon. Later they went to a picture house to reserve some tickets for the afternoon show. They returned home after buying some vegetables at the Crawford Market.

At breakfast that day, Nanavati asked her the reason for the change in her attitude, but failed to get any answer. He raised the matter again during lunch. As he approached Sylvia, the Prosecutor said, she asked him to keep away. Further questioning elicited a reply from his wife.

To a query as to how she happened to lose her love for him and whether there was anyone else for whom she cherished her affection, she said "yes". Nanavati then asked Sylvia if that person was Ahuja. To this too she replied in the affirmative. This naturally upset Nanavati.

She even acknowledged that she had not been faithful to her husband. This stunned Nanavati. From that moment Nanavati was hot.

"This gentleman in the dock is one of the ablest officers in the Navy and the Victim happens to be a flourishing Business Man dealing in motor cars." By these words public Prosecutor Mr. C. M. Trivedi, broke the silence of the Court and opened the case for the prosecution.

I glanced up: she was waiting for another chance at the cigar. It was hardly more than a butt but, when I held it toward her, she came and returned to the corner with it: now it was *all* hers.

In the corner she puffed the dying butt with her eyes closed, as if she'd lived her whole life for this moment. She didn't open her eyes till the butt went dead. Then, as though she'd known my eyes had been on her, she looked up at me with a mischievous air.

"Brrrr-andy," she demanded, in a low, long growl.

Martha had put the stuff too high on the shelf for the *ayah* to reach. Well, I could stand a snort myself.

When I brought the bottle down she crouched beside me, eyes alight with apprehension lest I drink it all and leave her not a drop. I had one drink but I didn't trust this one with the bottle. She understood and put her mouth up like a baby lamb. I let her have enough to stagger a ewe and drew it away. The stuff ran down the corners of her mouth, brown as her brandy-colored hide. She flashed me a smile white as milk and scrambled back to her corner. I put the bottle on the shelf and went back to the trial of Commander Nanavati:

SYLVIA'S EVIDENCE

Clad in pure white, Indian style, 28-year-old Sylvia Nanavati, English wife of Commander Nanavati, gave her evidence for the defence in the Bombay Sessions Court, in clear low tones, which had a touch of sadness at times and told the court "I was infatuated with Ahuja."

Sylvia's evidence was eagerly awaited by the parties as well as the public because it was she from whom some extraordinary story was expected. She was refused by the

238

*prosecutor to be called as a prosecution witness as prosecu-
tion did not place any reliance on her.*

*Examined by the defence counsel, Mrs. Nanavati said
that she was married to Commander in July, 1949 and had
three children, aged 9½, 5½ and 3. She came to know
Prem Ahuja three years ago. Before she knew Ahuja, her
married life was perfectly happy. Her friendship with
Ahuja resulted in intimacy with him, roughly speaking
about the beginning of 1958.*

*Mrs. Nanavati did not disclose this intimacy with Ahuja
to her husband till April 27 last (1959). Describing her
activities on that day, witness stated that in the morning,
she and her husband went to the veterinary hospital at
Parel, and on the way back to their residence at Colaba,
she purchased from Metro Cinema one ticket for herself
and three tickets for three children. Then she did shopping
at Crawford Market and returned home at 12-30 P.M.*

*Before lunch, they were sitting in the sitting room when
Commander Nanavati came and touched her. Witness
asked him not to do so because she did not like him.*

Defence counsel: Why did you not like him (husband)?

Mrs. Nanavati: At that time I was infatuated with Ahuja.

*Witness, continuing, said that Commander Nanavati
asked her why she was so cold and why she did not like
him. She replied that she did not want to talk about the
matter.*

*After lunch Commander Nanavati went to lie down in
the bedroom and witness was in the sitting room. After a
time her husband came out and told her they must talk this*

matter out. He further said that for the last few months "you have been cool to me." He also asked for the reason, and said, "Don't you love me?"

Witness did not give any reply. Commander Nanavati then asked her whether she was in love with anyone else, and she said yes. He then wanted to know who the other person was, but witness said nothing.

Witness continued: When he asked me whether it was Ahuja I said yes. He asked me whether I had been faithful to him. I told him I had not been faithful to him.

Commander Nanavati just sat dazed. Suddenly he got up rather excitedly and said that he wanted to go to Ahuja's flat and square things up. Witness became alarmed and put her hand to her husband and said, "Please don't go there, he will shoot you."

Commander Nanavati said: "Don't bother about myself. It does not matter, and in any case I will shoot myself."

Witness then caught hold of his arm and tried to calm him down. She told her husband "Why should you shoot yourself? You are the innocent one in this."

After this, witness said, her husband cooled down a bit and asked her whether Ahuja was willing to marry her and look after the children. She avoided answering that question, because she was too ashamed to admit that she had felt that Ahuja was trying to avoid marrying her. Thereupon her husband told her that he was prepared to forgive her if she promised never to see Ahuja again. But witness hesitated to give an answer.

240

Witness: I was still infatuated with Ahuja, so I hesitated to give the answer. As this was question which affected my whole future, I could not give an answer at the moment.

Continuing, witness stated that in the meantime, the doorbell rang and the neighbour's child came in for going to the cinema. Then they got ready for the cinema and her husband said that they should not talk about it any more and that they would talk about it the next morning.

Witness went to the cinema with three children, her husband driving the car. Though she requested Commander Nanavati to go with her for the show, he did not go, but just took them to the cinema. Counter foils of the tickets, which were taken charge of by the police were then tendered.

After leaving them at the theatre, her husband told her that he was going to the ship, I.N.S. Mysore, to get some medicine for the dogs.

Witness identified a silk shirt and coloured pants as having been worn by Commander Nanavati at the time her husband told her that he would return and pick them up at the cinema, the show ending at 5-30 P.M.

When she came out of the cinema she did not find her husband, but she was picked up by a relative of her husband. When she reached home, she came to know as the incident in the case. Her husband had taken the keys of their flat.

Question: I am definitely suggesting that your husband never said that he would kill himself?

Witness: My husband clearly said that. Asked how she was indifferent to that statement of her husband, she replied:

241

"I was myself in a state of upset. So I did not think clearly, but I was not indifferent to my husband shooting himself."

Question: Despite all that happened you went to the Cinema on that day?

Witness: It is difficult to explain things to the children. So as I had promised them, I took them to the Cinema.

Question: Where are you staying?

Witness: I am staying with the parents of my husband.

Question: "I am suggesting that you have agreed to oblige your husband now that lover is no more."

Witness: It is not true. I am stating what I actually know.

I fell asleep over the sorrows of Nanavati; and slept so soundly I did not hear Martha let herself in. I did not waken until she called to me from the bed.

My tactic was to make no love to her until she took the initiative: had she been making love, my approach would be tolerated only because I was supporting her for a short while.

So now, when she fell to sleep on my shoulder, I merely held her.

The drumming of the overhead fan began to drum to a slower beat; like the throb of great engines hauling below-deck. They were whispering the same warning over and over —or was it a seaman, whispering to himself while he listened, on the other side of my stateroom door? Baliram, in a white uniform and his face bloodied, stood, smiling knowingly, above me.

"Bombay is a great city, my friend," he said sorrowfully— and bent so low above me I felt his breath on my face and wakened.

242

It was Martha's breath, while she slept with her head on my shoulder. She had thrown her arm across me, and on the nape of my neck I could feel her fingers lying lightly. Her breasts, crushed against me, yet felt firm. She moved her thigh across mine and caught the calf of my leg with her heel, pressing herself against me. Her fingers tapped my nape: she was awake and waiting. I swept my hand down her back to the fullness of her hips and gently backward till she joined her hands about my back. Then joined her thighs.

When her breath began coming harder I took her mouth till her lips went cool in release. A moment later she had fallen back to sleep; her head upon her palm.

All night, in voluptuous gravity, this woman of Assam, wearing golden earrings, slept; her cheek upon her palm. All night the ceiling fan above her whirred. I saw her purchased breasts: their rise and fall.

While four roses made a shadow, as of many roses, on the wall.

Beyond the door her ancient *ayah* slept upon the floor.

All night, along the flaring street below, I heard the cabareting taxis' roar.

A night that roses, at one rupee for four, made a shadow, as of many rupees, on the wall.

*

I wakened to a tremendous crash, flinging my hands across my eyes—I thought the overhead fan had fallen.

Martha was pulling on a robe. There came a long low wail of fright. I got up and stumbled into the living room.

The top shelf of the great bookcase had crashed to the floor on top of the *ayah,* lying prone and wailing with the brandy bottle smashed across a litter of broken records. That she had tried to climb the shelves for the bottle and had gotten high

243

NOTES FROM A SEA DIARY

enough to reach it before the top shelf crashed was plain enough. Martha was rocking the baby while keeping up such a flow of abuse—in a tongue I'd never heard—that the kid was becoming more frightened than ever.

The *ayah* came crawling toward her on her belly, but Martha ignored her, joggling the baby in her arms. She paced up and down, strode to the bookcase and, with one hand demonstrating the enormity of the old woman's crime, shook the lower shelves angrily—and down they came with a louder crash than the one the old *ayah* had caused. In this fresh plunge every record, that had not fallen in the first fall, was smashed utterly.

And the *ayah*, as though sure now she must be responsible for *all* the bookshelves in the world, emitted a howl like a terrified child. She clutched, in her misery, at the hem of Martha's robe and Martha slapped her off so forcefully I felt I myself had been struck.

The old woman lay howling face-down in the rug.

"She's honest. You said so yourself," I reminded Martha. Martha didn't seem to hear.

"She's too old to get work," I insisted, "she'll die in the streets."

"Let her die," Martha decided.

In the morning the *ayah* was gone. Anna would be pleased, I knew.

It was time for me to leave as well.

So farewell to Ezekiel's and Ezekiel's creatures: goodbye to slicky-boy mackers with paralyzed mugs—may their rice-paddy angels all turn out to be carhops.

Good fortune for keeps to old ruined customs-men asweat in the noon bazaars: may police never entrap him in his Anglo-Indian home. And farewell to slipper-sloppering snitch-

244

on-Papa girlfinks: may they wind up in such cages as have room for one more.

Goodbye to all Mama-sans of low-voltage ports whose girls sell their clothes when no ship comes to dock. Farewell and soft blessings on all mascaraed ghosts who subsist on green ladydrinks along old Ho-Phang Road.

Farewell to the flares of Kamathipura and its sixty-watt night-bulbs burning all in a row. May all cockeyed whores, the whole wide world around, find rest under lamps that lean each to each.

Farewell to poor girls who put up with everything: and to upside-down tightwire walkers who wind up on all fours in fly-buzzing bars.

Good riddance to all cheesified, praise-me-and-I'll praise-you bone-deep begrudgers, whittling their words to gain six more floppy-hats at the next lecture—small-time cross-index-ing annotators: Fiedlers, Kazins, Podhoretzes, Macdonalds and such, sniffing the wind while counting the house—mere nosedrops in the nostrils of literature—screw the whole spite-burning lot.

Goodbye to all seamen whose heads are on crooked as well as to those whose heads are on straight. Goodbye to dead pursers who kept their ships out of trouble; and to radio officers, headphones clamped, who can't remember whether it was in Macao or Saigon.

Forever farewell to all mariners, beached or ashore, adrift between lonely hotel rooms and the shifting floor of the ocean's deeps.

Goodbye to all seamen who fear those deeps: yet fear the shore even more.

Goodbye to that ominous tenement—goodbye most of all and goodbye for keeps—goodbye to the woman of Assam.

Wherever she sleeps.

*

The *Malaysia Mail* was swinging out of the Port of Calcutta.

It was that hour when the ship, leaving the quais lighter for cargo discharged, seems heavier than ever with a weight of regret. Those short-term loves that might have been long-term; those glimpses of the Might-Have-Been that never would be now, leave officers and men alike feeling low. I needed a drink myself.

Concannon's door was open; the radio was beep-beep-jotting. But all to be seen of Sparks was two big feet, with shoes unlaced, stretched on his bunk. He opened one eye when I came in and rolled face to the wall. I helped myself to his gin, sat down and waited.

Fantasies, of having Martha with me in Chicago, came and went; in each of which she was companion and lover. Coming down one level of fantasy, she became faithful servant in a spacious house, with living quarters for herself and her son: the boy was growing up to share his mother's everlasting gratitude to the magnanimous American who had rescued them both from a life of shame, all of that. How to fit this into a sixty-a-month walkup in Chicago I hadn't quite resolved, when Concannon came awake at last.

"That was the worst one yet," he concluded.

"You look it," I assured him.

"I feel like it," he acknowledged, splashing cold water across his temples. He was already beginning to get his color back.

"What's the story on Manning?" I wanted to know.

"You know as much as I do," he told me, "a thousand

246

watches worth fifty apiece, and twelve thousand dollars, American, in undeclared bills."

"I didn't know about the money."

"It's a break for him, as it turns out," Concannon filled me in, "he'll be tried in the States instead of here."

"You mean he's still on board?"

"Karensen got hold of the American embassy—they wouldn't let the customs cops take him off the ship. He has to face charges on the twelve thousand first. Then India can extradite him. They didn't like it one bit."

"What becomes of the watches?"

"Customs confiscates them, then sells them at auction. The merchant who tipped them off will be allowed to get them back for a token bid."

"Do you think the old man was in on it?"

Sparks shook his head, no. "But he'll have trouble getting another ship all the same. Drink up."

He slipped the headphones on to indicate he had to get to work.

"Watch out you don't get the ship in trouble," I warned him.

I glanced into the officers' lounge on the way down to the crew's quarters. Danielsen, stirring something in a cup, seemed to be waiting for me. He gave me a faint birdlike shuttering of his eyes to indicate he wanted to say something. I tried a hearty, "How's things? What's your story?"

I had to put my ear down toward his mouth to catch his answer.

It sounded like "I'm not going ashore anymore."

"I don't blame you," I assured him, "if I'd had a gun I would have had to shoot you."

"I know," he smiled weakly, "I know."

247

"Has it happened before?" I asked, sitting down across from him.

He started to nod, yes. "But never aboard ship," he assured me, "never at sea."

There was an awkward silence.

"It's why I never go home at Christmas," he told me, "I *always* ship out."

"Something about Santa Claus does it?"

He shook his head. "I can drink at sea but not ashore."

"Well," I told him, "I thought I'd had *my* last drink, at sea or on shore, you can believe me."

"I'm sorry," he told me wistfully, "I apologize."

I didn't like it. His fury had diminished, yet had not died. When the light of sanity had come back into his eyes he had *still* wanted to kill me.

What I represented to him, that he needed to kill it, I surmise, had something to do with being—or seeming to him to be—of some specially privileged order.

"Have you seen Manning?" I asked, to change the subject.

"I haven't seen him," Danielsen told me, "the First Mate was taking care of the store when I was down there. Either Manning is ashamed to show his face or afraid to."

"What does he have to be afraid of?"

"The men won't get a draw again until we hit Long Beach. He was using their money to buy watches. There goes Smith's funny poker game."

I left Danielsen stirring whatever-that-was in a cup.

Cutting through the narrow Officer's Galley I had to squeeze past Smith and Captain Karensen in front of Manning's stateroom. Had either recognized me I would have exchanged greetings. But, as both moved aside to let me pass without a word, I took it as one of those small snubs that

248

men at work put on the man who has nothing to do but stroll idly about.

"Mister Manning!" I heard Smith call loudly as I left the galley. I continued on, down the ladder and into the crew's quarters.

Nobody was around but Bridelove and Muncie, playing call rummy for matches. Bridelove looked to be winning.

"What's our next port?" I asked him.

"The Philippines," Bridelove informed me. "I don't know whether we'll hit Tacloban City. Probably Ilo-Ilo and Cebu."

"Why not Manila?"

"Not this trip," Bridelove was certain.

Crooked-Neck Smith stood in the doorway, his head as far out on his neck as I'd ever seen it. It was really *stretching*.

"Manning just killed himself," he told us.

And turned and walked off.

*

Manning had been not only a scandal himself, but a cause for others to behave scandalously. The overdose he had taken had not been, necessarily, fatal. Had there been a single person aboard who cared, in the slightest degree, whether the man lived or died, he could have been saved.

Nobody had reported to the Captain that the purser hadn't shown up for duty. The Third Mate had rapped the man's door at six that morning and, receiving no answer, had informed the First Mate; who had simply dismissed the matter until ten, and had then opened the ship's store himself.

It had remained for Smith—who else?—on his customary round of making everybody's business aboard his own, to bring Karensen down to Manning's door. It had been Smith who'd broken in and dragged the man, without help, into the galley.

249

He'd tried mouth-to-mouth breathing, but the man's lips had turned blue even while he was trying. The Captain and the First Mate had had to carry the body down to the engine room.

There was no other place aboard to keep a corpse. Manning could not be buried at sea because the cause of death had not been determined. Karensen could scarcely risk an investigation like that on top of the one he was already facing because of Manning's black-market operations. Beyond sending a radio cable to the next of kin, Karensen could do nothing about Manning's body until he could turn the body over to a company doctor at Tacloban City or Ilo-Ilo.

That meant keeping the body in ice for a full week.

Whether Smith volunteered or was ordered to it I wasn't told: yet he seemed the logical man for the job.

"Talk about getting the ship in trouble," I heard Smith mourning the loss of his poker game, "I'm going to freeze the fat bastard's balls off!"

At first they distrusted his style. Then they distrusted his lack of politics. Then they distrusted his politics. Then they distrusted his drinking in public while they drank in secrecy. Or—worse yet—didn't drink at all. They distrusted his adventures. They distrusted his beard. Finally they distrusted his smile.

Yet they never came out with what they really distrusted.

Because the big thing with them was the money; and he never went for the money. He made the money, he liked the money, he spent the money. But he never went for the money.

They had his goat, they said. Because, sooner or later, they felt sure, he'd go for the money. He bought leisure and travel and adventure and houses and boats and sporting days and easy good times. Yet he never went for the money. Had he gone for the money they would have had his goat. As long as he didn't he had theirs: because it left them with nothing to get hold of except his beard and his smile.

The big thing with him was neither the money nor yet that mystic stream of time, eternal and serene; nor yet those long beautiful islands. Nor yet the changeless and changeful seas.

He was the historian who noted how many letters littered the field where the Austrian dead lay face-down in the sun with their hip pockets emptied: and he was the Austrian face-down in the sun. He was the English girl dreaming herself dead in an Italian rain. He was the advance man with purple wounds from elbow to wrist hiding beneath the sheets in a cheap hotel. He was the chronicler of mules with their fore-legs broken drowning in the port of Smyrna.

It wasn't the gulf stream of time, but the deep-floating corset borne upon it and the student's notebook that, in the end, were most important to him.

Hemingway was the picker with the long pole.

"Life is the greatest left-hander we know," he said—"unless it was Charlie White of Chicago."

And of the American writers of our time now dead, which one, given a single choice, would you bring back to life?

For myself it would have to be Hemingway.

Hemingway *all* the way.

Epilogue: Quais of Calcutta

Our rigging severed the moon the night we sailed
Into that jungle of cranes and jutting spars
The smear in that dungsmoke pall was merely day
Lighting impossible multitudes; that stirred as one.
Then rose, between the No-Beef Restaurant
And the Family Planning Store
Crying *No Mama No Papa No Baby No Chowchow Papa You
    Give.*

Kanani Mansions someone had named that ominous tenement
Where a woman of Assam wearing golden earrings slept
Her cheek upon her palm
Her ancient *ayah* slept upon the floor.
And all night long the ceiling fan whirred on.

O night so starred, with trees like clouds at rest
With lamps that leaned in pairs
And roses black as red—
I saw her purchased breasts
Their rise and fall.
A night that roses—one rupee per bunch—
Made shadows as of many rupees on the wall.

O chasmed love, with thighs that locked so sure
O deep-joyed dark, that makes the world come true:

EPILOGUE

Her roses choked within the burning air.
Yet in voluptuous gravity she slept on
Above the cabareting taxis' roar.
O night that sanctifies
The seaman's whore.

Dock-hawks followed our rigging to the sea
Then let us sail our ways alone.
Yet far, far out
With all docks gone and daylight swiftly going
Two messenger crows came cawing from the sun
Accusing me—
No Mama No Papa No Baby No Chowchow Papa You Give.

DATE DUE